Macke A. Will

WOODS

AND

WOODWORKING

for industrial arts

WOODS AND

for industrial arts

SECOND EDITION

PRENTICE-HALL, INC.   Englewood Cliffs, N. J.

WOODWORKING

DELMAR W. OLSON

Chairman, Department of Industrial Arts
and Coordinator of Graduate Study in Industrial Arts
Kent State University, Ohio

PRENTICE-HALL INDUSTRIAL ARTS SERIES

AN INTRODUCTION TO APPLIED ELECTRICITY - ELECTRONICS,
  by Robert L. Woodward, J. Lyman Goldsmith, and Alfred E. Bloch
BASIC ELECTRICITY, by Abraham Marcus
BASIC ELECTRONICS, by Abraham Marcus
ELEMENTS OF RADIO, by Abraham Marcus and William Marcus
GENERAL METAL: PRINCIPLES, PROCEDURES, AND PROJECTS, by
  Roland R. Fraser and Earl L. Bedell
INDUSTRIAL ARTS FOR THE GENERAL SHOP, by Delmar W. Olson
MECHANICAL DRAFTING ESSENTIALS, by Francis T. McCabe, Charles
  W. Keith, and Walter E. Farnham
RADIO PROJECTS, by Abraham Marcus
WOODS AND WOODWORKING FOR INDUSTRIAL ARTS, by Delmar
  W. Olson

Photographs used for Section Openings are by permission of the following:
I. American Forest Products Industries, Inc., K. S. Brown photo. II. Redwood Empire Association. III. The Mengel Company, Inc., H. E. Logsdon,
Mengel News Service photo. IV. Crossett Division of Georgia-Pacific Corporation, William E. Davis photo. V. Aluminum Corporation of America.

Library of Congress Catalog Card No. 65-10093
PRINTED IN THE UNITED STATES OF AMERICA
96246-E

Preface

This book considers woods and woodworking from a modern technological point of view, with emphasis on research and development in wood. Instruction in both hand processes and machine processes is given.

The following objectives have been stressed:

To encourage a change in emphasis from hand tool methods to machine methods, making this area of industrial arts more industrial.

To approach woodworking projects experimentally and creatively, rather than by the "cook book" method.

To clear up the mysteries in designing with wood, and to promote a *design-it-yourself* concept, with an emphasis on creativity.

To point out relationships and applications of the sciences to woods and woodworking so that the educative experiences may be more meaningful and intellectual.

To establish a "laboratory" as well as a "shop" atmosphere for studying and working with woods.

To arouse initiative in all students through challenging, inventive problem-solving experiences.

To My Teacher Colleagues:

The field of woods is as full of opportunities for the discovery and development of new ideas, for research and experiment, as any branch of modern technology. We need to set students to thinking this way. To encourage such thinking, there are sections at the ends of chapters in this book which are called "For Research, Experiment, Development." They include questions, problems, suggestions, all of which are invitations to further study. You may be able to guide students who have taken chemistry or physics into projects which are scientific and engineering in nature.

There is, without doubt, more to industrial arts than making things, although we know that the latter is a worthwhile experience. You and I are being challenged to demonstrate this extra value. Personally, I believe that it lies in making the course intellectual, creative, and recreational. I hope you do, too.

Delmar W. Olson

Acknowledgments

Grateful acknowledgment is made to the many people who have had a hand in the preparation of this book. There are the thousands of students who, in one way or another, have lent inspiration. There are those professional colleagues who persistently prodded with inquiries on "How's it coming?" And there are the many technical experts in numerous industries who provided information, editing, and counsel. Special acknowledgment is made to the many firms and organizations whose names appear in the captions for those illustrations which they have so generously contributed.

For reading the manuscript and making helpful suggestions, my particular thanks go to James R. Hastings, Associate Professor, Industrial Arts Education Department, State University College at Oswego, New York, and to Alvin Youngquist, Chairman, Industrial Arts Department, Morrison R. Waite High School, Toledo, Ohio.

For firsthand criticism and suggestions on the original edition, I appreciate the assistance of Mr. Luke Koenig, Mercer Area Junior High School, Mercer, Pennsylvania, Mr. Duffrin H. Morris, Admiral King High School, Lorain, Ohio, and Mr. Robert A. Peterson, Warren Harding High School, Warren, Ohio.

Contents

4
Wood Structures   76

5
Abrasives   87

6
Fasteners   91

7
Using Adhesives   96

1

SECTION

WOOD TECHNOLOGY

chapter 1

HOW INDUSTRY PRODUCES LUMBER AND LUMBER PRODUCTS

From the planting of seeds to the production of boards, lumber manufacture has become a huge industry. The supply of trees is no longer dependent entirely on Nature. Today the lumber industry looks after the production of trees as well as of lumber. The planting is done by dropping seeds from low-flying airplanes, especially in burned-out areas where there is nothing left to produce seeds. Tree nurseries plant seeds by machine. Seedlings are planted by mechanical tree planters which can set out 10,000 per day. Insects and disease in the forests are controlled by chemical sprays and dusting from airplanes. In other words, large-scale tree farming is the means for providing succeeding generations of Americans with an adequate supply of wood.

LUMBERING

The selection of trees to be harvested is done by trained foresters. These trees are marked and are then cut by teams of men called *fallers*. With a powerful chain saw, two men *fell* a tree, remove the limbs, and *buck* it into *sawlog* lengths. These logs are dragged out of the woods with crawler tractors, loaded onto trucks or railroad cars, or dropped into a stream and floated to the mill.

The Sawing of Logs. At the mill the logs are kept in a log pond or in the mill yard until needed. They are pulled by a conveyor chain, the *bull chain*, into the mill and onto a carriage for the *sawyer*, the man who decides how the log should be sawed. Held in the carriage, the log moves back and forth through the blade of the *headsaw*. In the larger mills this is a huge band saw, in others a circular saw. The squared timber is then run through the *resaw* which by means of a series of blades saws it into several boards at once. *Edger saws* now cut the boards to standard width and *trimmer saws* cut the ends square. From the mill the lumber is conveyed to the sorting shed, where it is graded.

Drying and Seasoning. Most lumber is dried before it is used. Some of it is stacked out of doors to air dry. The rest of it is kiln dried. Here it is put in huge ovens, steamed to saturate it with water, and dried by heated, circulating air until the moisture content has been reduced to about 4 to 8 per cent (see Fig. 1-8).

Kiln drying changes the chemical and physical nature of wood. Warping and checking are minimized. Expansion due to moisture is lessened as is the contraction on drying. The process tends to stabilize wood—to give us greater control over it. Kiln dried lumber is used in most wood products today.

RESEARCH IN CUTTING PROCESSES

The original process, and still the most common, for cutting wood is sawing. Slitting and slicing are used in making veneers. In the quest for better ways, however, research is developing some revolutionary cutting processes. Both sound and light waves have been successfully used in such a manner that the material is cut without making sawdust. The light process, called *laser*, an abbreviation for "light amplification by stimulated emission of radiation," appears to be the more successful of the two.

LUMBER PRODUCTS

Wood which has been cut from the tree, dried, and processed into boards, plywood, panel, and such forms is called lumber. It is ready for use in the manufacture of wood products. There are two main classes of lumber: *building*

Fig. 1—1. Logging, 1896 style.

K. S. Brown photo. Courtesy American Forest Products Industries, Incorporated

Fig. 1—2. The first step in logging is to fell the tree.

American Forest Products Industries, Incorporated, photo. Courtesy Weyerhaeuser Timber Company

Fig. 1—3. Today logs are skidded in ▶ from the woods with modern, mechanized equipment.

American Forest Products Industries, Incorporated, photo. Courtesy Caterpillar Tractor Company

K. S. Brown photo. Courtesy American Forest Products Industries, Incorporated

Fig. 1—4. A raft of logs is floated down ▲ the river to a saw mill.

Fig. 1—5. One log makes a truckload. ▶

Russ Meyer photo. Courtesy Western Pine Association

Fig. 1—6. A head rig cuts logs into sections called "cants."

American Forest Products Industries, Incorporated, photo, by Bill Hedrich, Hedrich-Blessing, Courtesy Edward Hines Lumber Company

◀ Fig. 1—7. A gang saw makes individual planks out of whole sections of logs.

W. J. Moore photo. Courtesy American Forest Products Industries, Incorporated

American Forest Products Industries, Incorporated, photo. Courtesy Western Pine Association

▲ Fig. 1—8. Scientifically controlled kilns are used for seasoning lumber.
◀ Fig. 1—9. Automatic lumber sorter.

American Forest Products Industries, Incorporated, photo. Courtesy Western Pine Association

lumber is for purposes of construction, as in houses and buildings; and *cabinet* lumber is for furniture, interior woodwork, and the like. The first is used for rough work; the second is used for fine work which requires a higher quality of wood.

Building Lumber. This lumber is generally of the softwood class, such as yellow pine, white pine, Douglas fir, and spruce. All have a high ratio of strength to weight. Dimensions of building lumber are standardized; 6', 8', 10', 12', 14', 16', 18', and 20' lengths are available. Widths are commonly 2", 4", 6", 8", 10", and 12". Thicknesses are 1", 2", 4", 6", and even more. *Boards* are considered to be 1" or less in thickness; *planks* are thicker stock.

Dimensions of all finished lumber are undersize. It is cut full dimension from the log, and some is then lost in surfacing. A "two-by-four," for example, will measure not 2" x 4", but 1⅝" x 3⅝".

Cabinet Lumber. Generally cabinet lumber is made from the hardwood types of woods. Some companies deal exclusively with it, but it is not often available at the local lumber yard. It is sold by the *board foot,* a lumber measurement meaning one foot long, one foot wide, and one inch thick, or its equivalent. Cabinet lumber comes in standard thicknesses but in *random* widths and lengths. It can be purchased rough or surfaced. A typical specification, for example, is American black walnut, 1" Rough, or 1" S2S to ¾–1³⁄₁₆". "S2S" means "surfaced-2-sides." This lumber is always kiln dried, unless otherwise specified.

Square Stock for Turning. Turning squares in various widths and lengths are available.

Veneers. Veneer is thin sheet wood cut from the green log. Veneer logs are steamed and soaked in hot water to make the fibers soft and plastic and the bark

Fig. 1—10 (left). Giant lathes peel thin, paper-like sheets of veneer from knot-free Douglas fir logs. Fig. 1—11 (right). Small strips of fir veneer are being edge-glued into long panels. This modern technique has reduced waste in veneer and plywood industries.

American Forest Products Industries, Incorporated, photos. Left, courtesy Douglas Fir Plywood Association; right, courtesy *The Timberman*

is removed by high pressure jets of water. In lengths of from 4' to 8', these logs are mounted between centers and revolved against a knife that peels off the wood as though it were paper being unrolled. This is the *rotary-cut veneer*.

Veneer is also made by slicing the sheets from a log. This produces a different grain pattern and is more expensive. Thicknesses of veneers range from 1/100" to 1/4".

After cutting to length the sheets are kiln dried.

Plywoods. Plywood is made from veneer bonded together with the grain of the sheets at right angles to each other. After gluing, the sheets are assembled in huge presses which, by means of heat and pressure, bond them into a material that has greater strength than solid wood of the same thickness, resists distortion, and is available in large sizes. As a "sandwich" of wood, plywood is equally strong in both directions.

Fig. 1–12. To make plywood, glue is applied to veneer sheets with grain placed alternately. Presses bond the sheets together.

Common thicknesses of plywood are 1/4", 3/8", 1/2", 5/8", 3/4", and 1". Widths are 24", 36", and 48", and lengths are commonly 6' and 8'.

Softwood plywoods are used principally in building construction; hardwood plywoods are used mainly for furniture and cabinets. Some plywood is made with a lumber core. The center is of solid lumber with a thin veneer bonded to it. This is used for wall paneling and furniture.

Plywood Grades. Plywood is made in an *exterior* and an *interior* grade. The exterior is bonded with waterproof glues; it is used chiefly in building construction and boats. Douglas fir and mahogany are the common woods for this.

There are five grades of hardwood plywood: *custom, sound, good, utility,* and *backing*. The custom grade is of top quality, especially selected for color and grain. Good is somewhat less perfect, but suitable for a natural finish. The sound and utility grades are intended for painting because of splices in the veneer, off colors, and other such defects. The backing grade is used for cabinet backs, crates, and the like.

Hardwood may be obtained with the same grade veneer on each side, or with a poorer grade on one side. Common designations are G1S, G2S, and So1S, meaning "good-1-side," "good-2-sides," and "sound-1-side."

Paneling is plywood usually 1/4" or less in thickness used on walls. Variations include veneer glued to fabric backing.

Hardboards. Hardboards are sheet woods made from wood chips which have been separated into individual fibers by steam treatment. The fibers, each coated with lignin, the natural adhesive in wood, are then rearranged and bonded into a very dense board by means of heat and pressure. They are available with a variety of surface textures. In many ways these boards are superior to plywood. They do not split or splinter, have no grain direction, take paint very well, and need no sanding. Try hardboard for jigsaw cut-outs.

Dowel Rods. Dowel rods are lengths of round wood, usually of birch, and in common diameters of ⅛″ to 1″. Lengths are usually 36″. Dowel pegs are used in wood structures (see Fig. 4-7).

DEFECTS IN LUMBER

Recognizing flaws and weaknesses in wood is a first step toward understanding and appreciating fine quality. The expert, as he grades and sorts, looks for many faults that have been accepted in the standards for commercial lumber. As you select wood, certain defects may be objectionable for one use and not for another. For example, knots may be undesirable in a piece of wood to be used for furniture, while they may be prized in wall paneling. Here are some of the common defects which you can learn to recognize:

1. **Knots** are classed according to size, shape, and quality.
   a. *Pin knots* are less than ½″ in diameter.
   b. *Standard knots* are from ½″ to 1½″ in diameter.
   c. *Large knots* are more than 1½″ in diameter.
   d. *Sound knots* are as hard as the surrounding wood and their fibers are intergrown with it.
   e. *Rotten knots* are softer than the surrounding wood.
2. **Checks** are cracks or splits which run across the rings and usually appear at the ends of a board.
3. **Splits** are severe cracks which tend to run the length of the board.
4. **Stain** is merely a discoloration which affects the appearance. Blue stain is common in white pine.
5. **Warp.** The term *warp* is often used to include any misshaping of a board. The following terms identify particular misshapen forms.
   a. *Crook* is a longitudinal curvature of the edge.
   b. *Bow* is a longitudinal curvature of the face.
   c. *Cup* is a curvature across the grain.
   d. *Twist* is a winding.

HOW TO SELECT WOOD
FOR PROJECTS

There is usually a best wood for any project you make. Study the characteristics of woods and you will see that all are not alike. Because black walnut, for example, may be your favorite wood, you may be tempted to use it for all your

Fig. 1—13. This wet-lap, or blanket of wood fibers, 4½″ thick before excess water is removed, will be pressed into 5/16″ Presdwood.

Courtesy Masonite Corporation

projects. This may not make good sense, however, because neither black walnut nor any other wood is best for all uses. Walnut is not usually suitable in the kitchen or bathroom; it belongs in the living room or dining room.

Here are some things to think about as you select the wood for a project:

1. Consider the function of the project. Does its use affect the choice of wood? Where will it be used, indoors or outdoors?

2. Consider the workability of the wood. Will the project be made by machine or by hand?

3. Consider the cost. Does the project deserve a scarce, high-priced wood or will a more common one be appropriate?

4. Consider the beauty. Is beauty of grain pattern and color important in the project? Is the design of the project such that it will show off the beauty of the wood? Should the grain pattern be bold and complex, or would a simple, straight-grained ef- fect be preferable? The most highly figured wood may not necessarily be the most beautiful when it is a part of the project. For example, a free- form coffee table top may be beauti- ful in a simple straight-grain pattern. The same shape may appear overly ornate and cheap when done in highly figured wood.

5. Consider the finish. Will a painted finish be used? Should the finish be waterproof? Is a clear, natural finish preferred?

6. Consider the defects. Watch for checks, warps, and knots. Make kiln dried lumber your first choice. Air dried wood in a project is likely to crack, warp, or open up at the joints. This may happen soon after assembly or after several months.

Your final choice will probably be a compromise, but whatever it is, have a good reason for it. And when you go to the lumber rack to get the boards, remember that *the best piece of wood is not always in the middle of a board.*

FOR RESEARCH, EXPERIMENT, DEVELOPMENT

1. How can one tell good lumber from poor?
2. Why are only certain kinds of woods chosen for boats?
3. For what uses are hardboards better than plywoods?
4. Why does a "two-by-four" not measure 2″ x 4″?
5. Why will plywood hold its shape better than a solid wood of the same thickness?
6. What is likely to happen to a piece of furniture if you made it of green lumber and placed it in your home?
7. What would probably be the nature of your job if you were a forester?
8. What kinds of lumber will most likely be found in a lumber yard in your town?
9. Why are construction lumbers not suitable for furniture?
10. Using liquid plastic, make a piece of chip board. Clean the chips of dust and remove small particles. Stir the chips into the plastic until each is coated. Pour the mix into a shallow tray to set.

chapter 2

HAND TOOLS

Hand tools are those devices that make it possible to work materials when hands alone are not enough. The machine tool makes the work easier, quicker, and more accurate than the hand tool, but does not altogether replace it. Your goals in woodworking may well include the desire to become an expert in each type.

LAYOUT AND MEASURING TOOLS

Layout and measuring tools are designed to help one work accurately, preventing mistakes and making guessing unnecessary.

Rules. Rules are used both for measuring and for marking straight lines. Common types include the *rigid* rule of steel or wood; the folding rule, or "zig-zag"; and the *flexible* rule of spring steel. The latter can be used to measure circumferences. For the most accurate measuring with a rigid rule, stand it on edge. When marking a line with a knife, to get maximum accuracy, use the steel rule rather than the wood.

Squares. Squares are used when testing for right angles—or "checking for square," as the woodworkers say—as well as for marking (see Fig. 2-2). The *try square* is most suitable for squaring ends of stock, for testing faces or surfaces for trueness, and for marking out cuts in joint making. The *combination square* has a sliding head and a miter gauge for 45-degree angles. The *framing square* is the large one-piece square used by a carpenter. With the various mathematical tables stamped on it, he can compute angles for cuts.

The sliding T-bevel has a movable blade that can be locked in any position. Any angle can be tested or transferred with it.

Marking Gauge. This is a combination marking and measuring device (see Fig. 2-3). The distance is set from the point to the guide with a rule. Because the point makes a groove, do not use it to mark on finished surfaces.

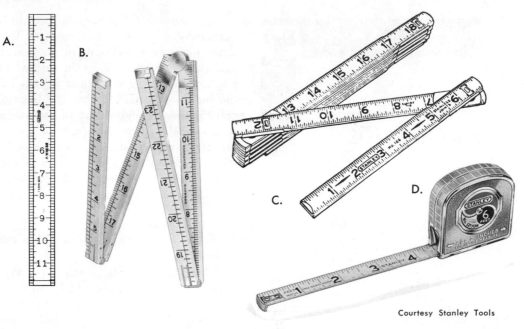

Fig. 2—1. Several types of rules. Each one serves a different purpose. A. Bench rule. B. Folding rule. C. Zig-zag rule. D. Push-pull rule.

Courtesy Stanley Tools

Calipers. Calipers (see Fig. 2-4) are used to measure diameters. The *inside* calipers measures inside diameters, and the *outside*, outside diameters. The distance between the points is read and set on a rule.

Trammel Points. These are clamped on a rule and used as a compass for marking large curves (see Fig. 2-5).

Awl. The sharp point is used for pricking the exact centers for boring holes.

The pencil and the rule with the aid of a thumb can be used for marking wide widths. Grip the rule at the desired distance so that the thumbnail can slide along the edge of the board. Hold a pencil at the end of the rule reasonably square with the guide edge.

The pencil-and-fingernail combination (see Fig. 2-6) is a quick way of marking chamfers, dados, and rabbets.

SAWS

It is not difficult to saw a board with a hand saw, but you will agree, now or later, that to saw to a line takes considerable control of this simple tool. "Elbow grease" alone is not enough. Always cut on the outside of the line, but as close to it as possible without touching it. This saves much work in planing. If you plan to saw the board again to more accurate length, be sure to allow enough stock for it, perhaps ¼". The saw cut itself is called the *kerf*. A dull saw is most obstinate—it even refuses to follow a line.

HAND SAWS

Hand saws are the common saws, used for rough cutting. The *crosscut* saw is for cutting wood across the grain, and

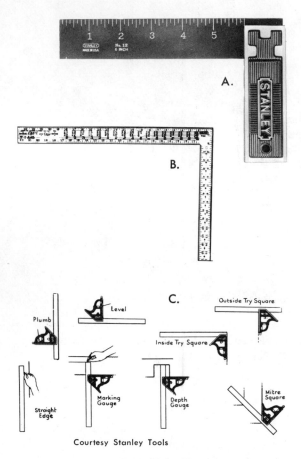

Courtesy Stanley Tools

Fig. 2—2. Some common squares. A. Try square. B. Framing square. C. Combination square in use.

cut accurately. Once it is kinked, it is permanently crippled and useless. Use a hand saw on wood only, or on similar material. Always hang up the saw when you are not using it. When it falls off the bench, it usually strikes the handle, cracking it. A light coat of polishing wax should be applied periodically to prevent rust. A rusty saw requires more effort than a shiny one. If you would keep it sharp, never lay any saw on tools or other metal objects.

How to Crosscut:
1. Begin by squaring the line across the board.
2. Clamp the board flatwise in a vise when possible, otherwise lay it on a saw horse.
3. Using the thumb as a guide, start the cut with a long, slow pull stroke. Then proceed with short strokes until the cut is well started.
4. Gradually lengthen the strokes until most of the teeth are used. Move the thumb away. When the saw sticks, you are probably pressing too hard. A sharp saw requires very little pressure.
5. Ease up with short strokes as you finish the cut. Hold up the piece being cut off to avoid splitting.
6. Keep your eye on the saw cut. When it first appears to be wandering from the mark, back up and re-saw the kerf. Don't wait until the cut has strayed across the board. A slight twisting of the blade toward or away from the mark will gradually correct the cut.

How to Rip. The procedure is the same as for the crosscut saw, except that a short or narrow board is sawed while held vertically in a vise. Use a saw horse for ripping a long board.

the *rip* saw is for cutting with the grain, or ripping.

Sizes of Hand Saws. Blade lengths vary from 16 to 26 inches. The coarseness of the teeth is expressed as *points per inch*. A general purpose crosscut saw is about 22 inches long with 10 points, and a rip saw, 24 to 26 inches, with 5 points. The number of points is stamped on the heel of the blade.

Care of Hand Saws. A saw blade must be kept straight and true if it is to

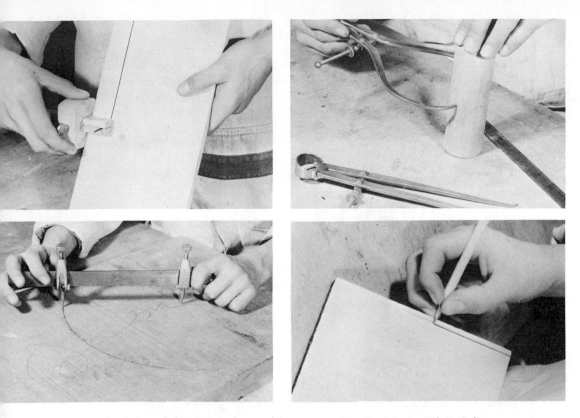

Fig. 2—3 (top, left). Using the marking gauge. Fig. 2—4 (top, right). Calipers are used for measuring diameters. Fig. 2—5 (bottom, left). Marking out a circle with trammel points. Fig. 2—6 (bottom, right). A fingernail and pencil can be used to mark lines parallel to an edge.

THE BACK SAW

The back saw, so named because of its reinforced back, is used for making fine accurate cuts, as when cutting to accurate length and in making joints. Keep it hung up when not in use; it is a precision instrument.

How to Cut a Board to Length:

1. Just as in crosscutting, square a line across the board.
2. Clamp the board flat in a vise when possible, to leave both hands free for guiding the saw. Otherwise clamp it on the bench or use a bench hook.
3. Clamp a straight block of wood over the mark for a guide.
4. Keep the blade snug against the block as you move it slowly back and forth, cutting over the entire width at each stroke.
5. A sharp saw will cut cleanly through the bottom without splintering the board. Ease up on the pressure as the saw begins to cut through. Hold the free end of the board so that it does not break off unevenly.

THE MITER BOX

The miter box is a device in which the saw can be guided to cut wood accurately to desired angles. The back saw is swung to the desired angle and locked. The wood must be held firmly against the fence. Clamp it there when possible.

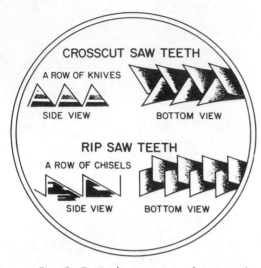

Fig. 2—7. A closeup view of saw teeth.

THE COPING SAW

This is the saw that probably inspired the invention of the jig saw. It is used for cutting curves in thin wood and is not intended for sawing straight lines. It cuts best on a vertical pull stroke, as a jig saw does, rather than as a hand saw. The scroll saw, hand version, is similar to the coping saw, except that it has a deeper throat.

Inserting a Blade. An assortment of blades is available for fine, medium, and coarse cutting, with either pin or loop ends. On some saws the blade is inserted by springing the frame against the bench. On others, the handle is loosened and the blade is inserted and tensioned by tightening the handle. The teeth should point toward the handle.

Cutting with the Coping Saw. Clamp the board flat on the edge of the bench and, holding the saw vertically, start cutting with short, quick strokes. Press forward only enough to keep the blade cutting. When it sticks, you are pressing

too hard. Keep the blade cutting as you turn the frame to go around curves. For fine details use a V-block to support the material. The blade should be kept close to the V.

To cut a hole with a coping saw, first bore a ¼" hole near the line, in the waste stock. Stick the blade through the hole and insert it in the frame. Then saw as before.

THE COMPASS SAW

This saw, with its long, slender, tapered blade, can be inserted in a hole for a start. It is used for rough cutting, as is a hand saw, but it can cut curves in heavy stock.

THE TURNING SAW

A turning saw looks like an old-fashioned buck saw. It is used for cutting curves in thick wood when the coping saw is inadequate.

Fig. 2—8. The rip saw cuts along the grain.

HAND PLANES

A hand plane is used for making wood surfaces smooth and flat, or true. Properly sharpened, adjusted, and used, it will cut end grain as smoothly as flat grain. There are several types for different purposes, but all have chisel-like blades adjustable for depth of cut.

Model Maker's Plane. This plane is used on miniature work as a one-hand tool.

Block Plane. Usually 4″ to 6″ long, this is for one-hand use on curves, end grain, chamfers, and fitting.

Smooth Plane. This is the next largest plane, usually 8″ to 9″ long. It is probably the best all-around plane for the beginning woodworker.

Jack Plane. This is the professional cabinet maker's general purpose plane, 11″ to 15″ long.

Fore Plane and Jointer Plane. The fore plane is about 18″ long and the jointer plane, 22″ to 24″. Both are used

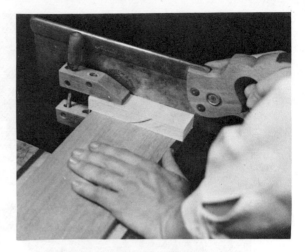

Fig. 2—10. The back saw is used for accurate cutting. A gauge block makes it even more exact.

Fig. 2—9. The crosscut saw cuts across the grain.

for jointing edges. The longer the bed, the truer the edge it joints. Why not use them for surfacing?

Care of Planes. More planes are damaged by dropping than by use. The beds are usually of cast iron and break easily with a fall. Keep the parts lightly lubricated and rust-free. When your plane is not in use, lay it on its side if you wish to keep it sharp. Can you figure out why? Set the blade only as deep as you can handle it. The smoothest cuts are light cuts. When the plane chews up the surface of the wood, plane from the opposite direction or take a lighter cut. A plane can be made to cut so smoothly that fine sandpaper will roughen the surface.

Adjusting a Plane. The depth of cut must be adjusted according to the kind of wood, the grain, and the amount of "push" you have.

1. Set the cap iron on the blade close to the cutting edge for hardwood, to

Fig. 2—11 (above). The use of a miter box permits accurate angular and square cuts to be made. Here the back saw is being used with a miter box.

Fig. 2—12 (below, left). Cutting with the coping saw is easier when the work is clamped to a bench. Fig. 2—13 (middle). A V-block is used to support the material when cutting fine detail with the coping saw. Fig. 2—14 (below, right). To cut a hole with the coping saw, the blade is inserted through a bored hole.

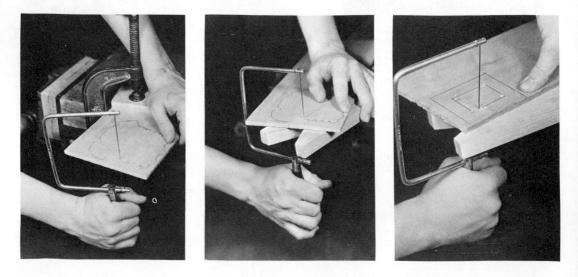

give it support. For soft woods move it back to about ⅟₁₆ inch from the edge to permit a thicker shaving. Tighten it securely with a heavy screwdriver.

2. Assemble the plane and, sighting along the plane bottom, level the blade in the throat by means of the lateral adjusting lever. Now screw the blade in or out, make a test cut, and readjust the blade, if necessary.

3. When a plane is working properly, it cuts easily and smoothly. If you have to "fight" it, the blade is dull or improperly adjusted.

How to Plane the Face of a Board:
1. With the work held firmly in a vise or clamped to the bench top, make a few trial cuts.
2. Using a try square, locate the high spots and plane them off. Plane with

Fig. 2—15. The common hand planes. Use the one which best fits the job.

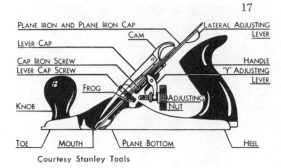

Courtesy Stanley Tools

Fig. 2—16. Hand plane: working parts.

the grain unless there is much to remove. In this case planing across the grain may be faster.

3. Hold the plane at a slight angle to the grain, but push in the direction of the grain. Lift the plane on the return stroke.

How to Plane an Edge:
1. Mark the line to which you will plane. Clamp the board in a vise close to the line.
2. Hold the plane firmly and squarely on the edge, and at a slight angle to it. Push it slowly from one end to the other. Repeat until the edge has been planed over its entire length.
3. Test for trueness with a straight edge. Then, with a try square, check the edge for squareness with the face.

How to Plane an End:
1. The blade must be very sharp and set for a thin cut. Square a line across the end of the board, as near the end as possible. Clamp it in a vise close to the mark and at a convenient height.
2. Holding the plane firmly and squarely on the end, and at a slight angle to it, push it slowly about three-fourths of the way across. Then plane from the other direction. If you plane

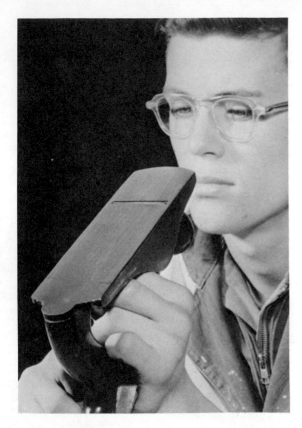

clear across, the wood will split at the far corner. Planing from each edge toward the center will prevent this. If you have plenty of waste stock on one edge, saw off the corner at an angle in this waste; then plane across the board toward the corner. This prevents splitting, too.

How to Square a Board:

Using the procedures already described for planing and checking for trueness, follow these steps to square a board.

1. Select the better side of the board for the *No. 1 face*. Plane it true if necessary. When the board is at the desired thickness to begin with, skip steps 1 and 6.
2. Plane an edge straight and square with this face.
3. Plane an end straight and square with this edge and this face.
4. Mark the board to length and saw it off close to the mark with a back saw. Plane this end square.
5. Mark width from the true edge. If there is much waste, rip it off. Plane to the mark, keeping it square with the face and with each end.
6. Mark the thickness around the edges and ends. Plane the *No. 2 face* to this mark.

▲ Fig. 2—17. Checking the adjustment of the plane blade. It should lie parallel to the bed and to the slot.

▼ Fig. 2—18. Planing a face. Hold the plane at a slight angle to the grain of the wood. Push in the direction of the grain. Fig. 2—19. Planing an edge. Hold the plane at a slight angle and push it slowly along the entire length.

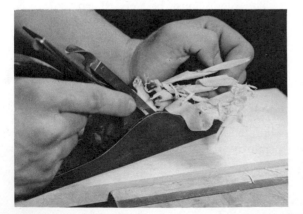

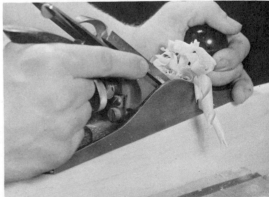

Courtesy Stanley Tools

Fig. 2—20. The combination plane. Fig. 2—21. The router plane. Fig. 2—22. The rabbet plane.

If you don't get the board square and the correct size the first time you try it, take comfort. Few beginners do on the first try.

The Combination Plane. This is a special purpose tool for cutting shaped moldings, beads, flutes, and such. Cutters of different shapes are inserted and the tool is then operated as a hand plane.

The Router Plane. For cleaning out waste stock in dados and for surfacing the bottoms of hollows, the router plane is very handy. The cutters are adjusted to the desired depth and the tool is operated by pushing or by pulling.

Fig. 2—23. Planing an end. Hold the plane at a slight angle so that the blade slices the wood cleanly.

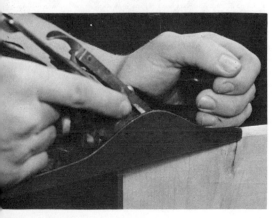

The Rabbet Plane. Rabbets may be cut by hand with this special plane. It has adjustable guides for width and depths of cut.

THE SPOKE SHAVE

This tool was used by the old blacksmith and wagon maker for shaping spokes for wooden wheels. You will find it useful for shaping archery bows, table legs, and other sculptured forms. The blade is sharpened like a plane iron. It is held in adjustment by thumb screws. With this tool, too, the light cuts are smoothest.

CABINET SCRAPERS

A cabinet scraper is used following the hand plane, jointer, or planer in smoothing a flat face. When sharp, it peels off exceptionally fine shavings, and it will smooth curly-grained and knotty areas when a plane roughens them. When dull, the scraper makes only dust and perspiration. There are several types of wood scrapers, but the cabinet scraper with the flat, removable blade is preferred for fine work. The blade can be used by itself, or in the holder.

Fig. 2—24. A cabinet scraper is used on the face of the stock after planing.

WOOD FILES

Files are used for smoothing curves, usually on the edges of stock, following sawing. The two common types are the *wood rasp* with coarse, individually cut teeth, and the *cabinet file* with chisel-like teeth across its width. The usual lengths are 8″, 10″, and 12″, although they are available from 4″ to 14″. The common shapes of cabinet files are flat, half-round, round, square, and triangular. They may be had in two different cuts, *single cut,* or coarse; and *double cut,* or smooth. The coarsest in each of these two cuts is the *bastard cut* and the finest is the *smooth cut.* The *second cut* is in between. The wood rasp has little use in woodworking today, and when it is used, it is only for very rough work. Always use a handle on a file; it gives better control and eliminates the danger of a sharp tang.

Shaping With a File:
1. Clamp the board in a vise with the edge to be filed, as horizontal as possible. Clamp the edge close to the vise to prevent chattering.
2. With one hand holding the point and the other the handle, push the file diagonally across the edge with just enough pressure on it to make it cut.

3. Use a flat file for convex surfaces and the half-round for hollow. A file is useless for squaring an edge as you will probably discover.
4. Clean the teeth frequently with a file card or a wire brush.
5. Watch the edge as you file. The surface should be smooth and clean-cut, with file marks replacing saw marks. If it seems to be unusually rough, file from the opposite side of the wood or use a finer file. Work down to the mark so that little sanding will be required.

CHISELS AND GOUGES

The wood chisel is used for fitting joints in wood and for shaping edges. The two common types are the *tang* and the *socket,* referring to the handle. The tang chisel has its handle forced onto the tang; the socket type has its handle set into a tapered cup. Various widths are available, from ¼″ to 2″ and more. A wood chisel is sharpened like a plane iron and peels off shavings in the same manner.

Fig. 2—25. Smoothing a curved edge with a wood file.

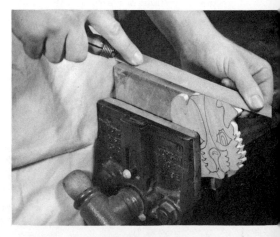

Using a Wood Chisel:

1. Always use a sharp chisel; it must be sharp enough to cut with very little pressure. Lay it bevel side down on the bench to protect the edge.
2. Use as wide a chisel as the job will permit.
3. When possible, clamp the work in a vise or on the bench so that you can use both hands on the chisel. Use a mallet only when extra force is required.
4. Use the chisel with the flat side to the work for paring cuts. When cleaning out dados or when the handle gets in the way, turn it over and slide it along on the bevel.
5. When making paring cuts or shaping cuts, use one hand on the blade and the other on the handle, so that the cutting can be accurately and safely controlled.

Gouges. Gouges are chisels with hollow blades for use in roughing out concave forms. If you make a free form tray, for example, you will probably use a gouge and a mallet to do the hollowing. Start at the outside and work around the shape, gradually moving toward the center.

Carving Chisels. These are small wood chisels and gouges in a variety of shapes to suit various cuts. They must be razor-sharp to make clean cuts. Mallets are not used with carving chisels.

Fig. 2—26. The "Surform," is available as A. a file, B. a pocket model, and C. a plane. Its teeth can out-perform the file and the plane on many jobs. It is better than the spoke shave for wood sculpturing.

Courtesy Stanley Tools

SAFETY SENSE

1. It's the dull chisel that causes most accidents!
2. Always chisel away from yourself and never let one hand or finger get out in front while cutting. To hold the work in one hand and to chisel with the other is not only the hard way, but also the dangerous way.
3. Why would anyone ever put a chisel in his pocket?

KNIVES

Knives have considerable use in woodworking today even though carving and whittling are not the major activity in industrial arts that they were in manual training years ago. The Sloyd system of manual training, developed in the Scandinavian countries and brought to the United States during the last part of the past century, taught boys how to become skillful with the carving knife. For many of their projects, only the knife was used. The name *sloyd knife* is still given to a

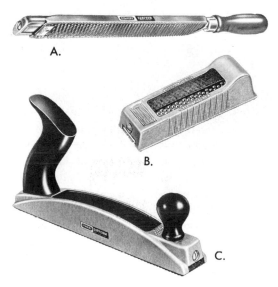

A.

B.

C.

type of woodworking knife having a short, sturdy blade. Today however, the carving knives with thin replaceable blades are preferred because they have blades of different shapes, are easy to keep razor-sharp, and the blades can be removed when not in use.

In addition to carving and whittling, the knife is used for making very accurate marks across the grain in laying out work. It is often preferred for shaping convex surfaces, as in model building. Use it to cut dowel rods up to ¼" in diameter. Lay the dowel on a bench and, pressing the knife into it, roll the rod slowly.

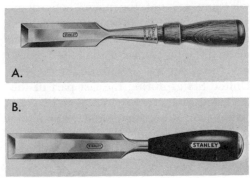

Courtesy Stanley Tools

Fig. 2—27. Two wood chisels. A. Socket type with butt (short) blade. B. Heavy duty type with pocket (longer) blade.

  SAFETY SENSE

1. Use only a very sharp knife. A dull one requires excessive pressure, which may cause the knife to slip.
2. Always cut away from yourself.
3. Never carry an open knife in a pocket, even for a moment.
4. Use a knife blade for cutting only; for prying, a screw driver is much better.
5. Put the knife away in its proper place as soon as you have finished with it.

BORING AND DRILLING TOOLS

The woodworker bores holes in wood with an auger bit and drills them with a drill bit.

The Brace. The combination of auger brace and auger bit is used for boring holes ¼" and larger. The brace is also used with other tools, such as countersinks and screw driver bits. Braces with ratchets are for working in close quarters when a full turn is impossible. The jaws can grip either round or square shanks, but hold best to the square. Brace sizes are given according to the sweep. This is the diameter of the circle swung by the handle as the brace is turned. A 12" sweep is common.

Auger Bits. Auger bits are used only in wood or other soft material. The most common sizes range from ¼" to 2", by sixteenths. The number on the tang is the diameter of the hole in sixteenths. For example, a No. 5 bores a ⁵⁄₁₆" hole.

Care of the Brace and Bits. A drop of oil is occasionally needed in the head of the brace, and in the ratchet mechanism. The bits need sharpening periodi-

Fig. 2—28. Use both hands with the wood chisel whenever possible.

cally (see p. 25). If a bit gets bent, lay it on a wood top bench and roll it over slowly until the high side comes up. Tap this with a mallet or soft face hammer.

How to Bore Holes:

1. Unscrew the chuck on the brace a few turns; insert the tang of the bit, and tighten.
2. Press the point of the lead screw on the bit into the wood at the center of the desired hole. Press against the head of the brace with one hand, and with the other, turn the handle clockwise. To cut fastest, press firmly, but turn slowly so that the screw can pull the bit through the wood without slipping.
3. When the point comes through the back side, stop and reverse the direction and then remove the bit. Finish boring from the back side. This prevents splintering at the edge of the hole.
4. If the hole must be square with the board, use two try squares as guides. Set them about 90 degrees apart on the board.

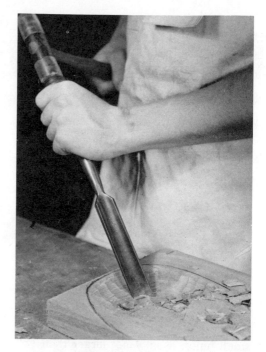

Fig. 2—29. Hollowing out a tray with a gouge and a soft-face hammer. When making such a project, do your hollowing before the board is cut to shape. It is easier to hold in a vise, or to clamp to the bench.

Fig. 2—30. A carving tool is used to cut away the background. The outlining of the letters was done with a "V", or veining tool.

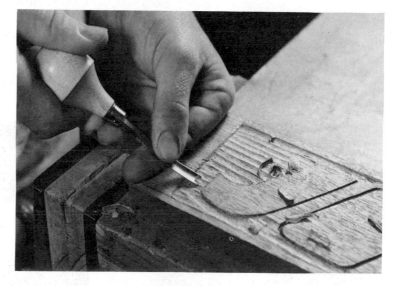

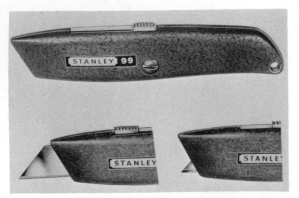

Courtesy Stanley Tools

Fig. 2—31. A modern carving knife with a replaceable and retractable blade.

THE HAND DRILL

The hand drill is used for drilling small holes, usually not larger than ¼". It turns straight shank twist drills at a fairly good speed. Some hand drills have open gears and others have enclosed.

How to Use a Hand Drill:

1. To insert the bit, grasp the chuck in one hand and with the other, turn the crank backwards, counter-clockwise, to open the jaws. Insert the bit, hold the chuck, and turn the crank in the opposite direction until the bit is tightly gripped.

2. Prick a center mark at the desired point with an awl. Insert the tip of the bit and, holding the drill handle in one hand, turn the crank clockwise. Use only enough pressure to keep the bit cutting. Too much will bend the bit or cause it to stick. Ease up as the bit cuts through the back side.

3. To remove the bit, turn the crank in the drilling direction and pull on the handle. This cleans out the hole and keeps the chuck from loosening.

☞ SAFETY SENSE

You can get a finger pinched in the gears when tightening or loosening the chuck. Watch where and how you hold the drill or, better yet, use a hand drill with enclosed gears.

DRILL BITS

Straight shank drill bits are used in hand drills, portable electric drills, and in drill presses. An auger brace does not hold them securely. There are two types of these drill bits: the *carbon steel* and the *high speed* (H.S.). These letters are stamped on the shank of the latter type

Fig. 2—32 (left). Boring a hole with an auger bit and brace. Fig. 2—33 (right). Drilling a hole with an enclosed gear hand drill.

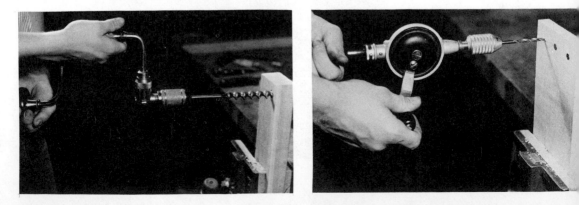

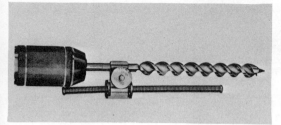

Courtesy Stanley Tools

Fig. 2—34. An adjustable depth gauge for an auger bit.

Courtesy Stanley Tools

Fig. 2—35. An automatic drill to drill pilot holes for small screws.

for identification. Carbon steel bits are for wood and other soft materials. They cut these as well as the high speed bits and are much less expensive. Common sizes range from $\frac{1}{32}''$ to $\frac{1}{2}''$, by sixty-fourths. The size is stamped on the shank, but is often impossible to read. You can determine the size by finding its proper hole in the drill bit holder.

How to Use Twist Drill Bits:

1. Use only sharp drill bits (see p. 22). A dull bit rubs the wood and gets hot. If forced to cut, such a bit will burn or break. Wood is a poor conductor of heat and a dull bit overheats quickly, especially in hard woods when a power drill is used. Use a slow speed for drilling holes on the drill press and feed the bit as fast as it can cut.

2. Press only hard enough to keep the bit cutting. This keeps friction to a minimum and prevents the bit from bending.

3. No lubricant or coolant is used for drilling in wood. Draw the turning bit from the wood frequently to remove chips and to cool it.

4. Carbon steel bits can be straightened in the same manner as auger bits.

THE AUTOMATIC DRILL

This tool is used for drilling small holes. The special bits are kept in the handle. Pumping the handle up and down makes the bit revolve.

THE BIT GAUGE

When you want to bore several holes to the same depth, clamp a bit gauge on the auger bit and bore down until the gauge touches the work. For small twist drills, a gauge can be improvised from a block of wood. Drill through and cut it off so that the bit protrudes the desired depth.

Fig. 2—36. An expansive bit bores large holes. Set the sliding cutter to the proper position and make a test cut in scrap before boring the desired hole.

Courtesy Irwin Auger Bit Company

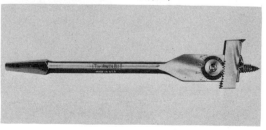

Fig. 2—37. Countersinking a hole for a flat head wood screw. Counterbore, then drill the screw hole.

THE COUNTERSINK

The countersink cuts a cone-shaped well into which the head of a flat head wood screw fits. One type is used in an auger brace and another, with a straight shank, is used in the drill press or portable drill. The size is given as the greatest diameter which the tool will cut. When countersinking a screw, cut the well just deep enough to allow the screw to lie flush with the surface (see Fig. 6-4). If you wish to conceal the head, as with a wooden plug, the hole should be *counterbored* with a bit slightly larger than the screw head (see p. 93-94).

SCREW DRIVERS

The original purpose for a screw driver was to drive screws, but the tool is so handy for opening paint cans, prying open boxes, and such that manufacturers usually make them rugged enough to do this. Following are the common types of screw drivers used in woodworking: *common, offset, ratchet, spiral,* and *Phillips.* The size is given as the length of the blade from handle to tip. The blade must always fit the screw slot, both in length and width, otherwise it mutilates the slot. The end should be square and blunt, not sharp.

Fig. 2—38. An assortment of screw drivers. A. Common. B. Phillips, or recessed head. C. Offset. D. Automatic.

Courtesy Stanley Tools

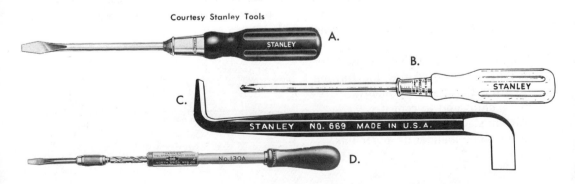

How to Use a Screw Driver:

1. Select as large a screw driver as will fit the slot.
2. Use the longest screw driver that is convenient to handle. You can get more twist on it.
3. Use one hand to keep the blade in the slot while you press and twist with the other. Press just hard enough to keep the blade in the slot.
4. Keep the blade in line with the screw.

Screw Driver Bits. These bits have square shanks to fit in auger braces. The screw driver bit is a timesaver when there are many screws to be installed and when they are too large to be driven with another type. It is necessary to hold the blade in the slot and to keep the brace in line with the screw.

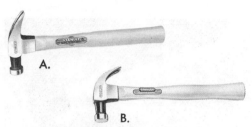

Courtesy Stanley Tools

Fig. 2—40. Common nail hammers. A. Curved claw. B. Straight, or ripping claw.

Offset Screw Driver. This is an L-shaped screw driver to be used when the screw is inaccessible to the ordinary types.

Ratchet Screw Driver. A screw driver with a built-in rachet eliminates the need for re-gripping the handle for each twist.

Spiral Screw Driver. This tool is pumped up and down to turn the bit, for speed driving.

Phillips Screw Driver. This is a special screw driver used only for driving recessed head screws (see Fig. 6-2).

HAMMERS AND MALLETS

Several types of hammers are used in woodworking, each for a different purpose.

The Claw Hammer. This is the common hammer for driving and pulling nails. Size is given according to the weight of the head. A 7-ounce hammer is for small nails and brads, a 16-ounce hammer for general use. The driving face of the claw hammer is slightly rounded, not flat, to make nail driving easier. Can you figure out why? The claw hammer must not be used on cold chisels or for other rough work where this surface may be damaged.

Fig. 2—39. Driving a wood screw requires two hands.

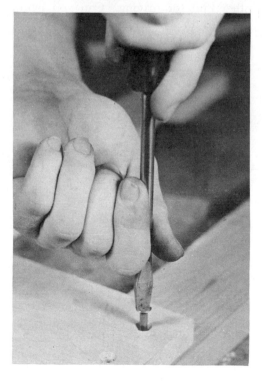

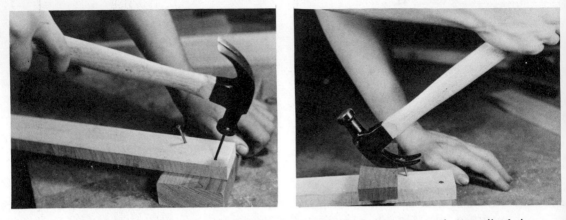

Fig. 2—41 (left). This shows the proper method of driving a nail. Use all of the handle and slant the nails to hold them better. Fig. 2—42 (right). If you need to pull a nail, use a claw hammer in this manner. Notice the use of the block which gives extra leverage and protects the stock.

Driving a Nail:
1. Grasp the handle of the hammer near the end where it feels most comfortable. Tap the nail slightly to start it, so that it stands by itself.
2. Drive the nail down flush with the surface. At first it takes courage to strike the nail with hard blows, but with practice you should be able to drive a 6d nail with three or four blows. A nail driving contest is fun. Try it at your next industrial arts party.
3. The smaller and more slender the nail, the lighter the blow.
4. When a nail bends in driving, it is better to remove it than to take a chance on its marring the work surface.

Pulling a Nail. The claws of the hammer are intended for pulling nails. Slide the claws under the head and pull back on the handle. A block of wood under the claws prevents damage to the work and increases the pulling leverage.

Upholsterers' Hammer. This is a tack hammer with one end of the head magnetized for holding and starting tacks. Once the tack is started in place, use the other end for driving. Can you figure out why the magnetized end is split?

Mallets. Mallets have soft heads, usually of wood, rawhide, or rubber. They are used when driving force is needed without the chance of damaging the work or the tool, as in aligning parts, driving joints together, driving wood chisels, and the like.

Soft Face Hammers. These are mallet-type hammers except that the head has soft faces only. When of plastic they are usually replaceable.

THE NAIL SET

The nail set is the slender punch for setting the heads of wire brads and finishing nails below the surface. Choose one the same size or smaller than the head and drive it down about 1/16".

CLAMPS AND CLAMPING

Clamps are very handy devices in woodworking. They are used to hold work that cannot be held in a vise. They also supply the necessary pressure for good gluing. They are used when setting up a project to test the fitting for the pieces before the final assembly. There are many types of clamps, but those used most often are *"C" clamps, hand screws,* and *bar clamps.*

"C" Clamps. Shaped like the letter "C," these clamps are used when holding wood face-to-face. Sizes are given as inches of opening.

Hand Screw Clamps. These clamps have wooden jaws capable of applying pressure over a large area. They can hold work when the surfaces are not parallel. Common sizes have openings which range from 6″ to 14″.

Bar Clamps. Bar clamps are for holding large work, especially for gluing stock edge to edge, as in a table top. They are especially helpful in the assembly of furniture. Sizes are given in feet, referring to the maximum opening.

How to Use Clamps for Gluing:

1. Select the best clamps for the job.
2. Get some scrap blocks to place between the clamp jaws and the work, to prevent damage.
3. Assemble the work with the clamps to get the proper adjustments. Then disassemble it, laying the clamps in a convenient order.
4. Apply the glue. Get a buddy to help you assemble and clamp the pieces.
5. Apply enough pressure to draw the parts snugly together but not enough to distort or damage the parts.
6. Wipe off any excess adhesive immediately with a damp cloth. This can

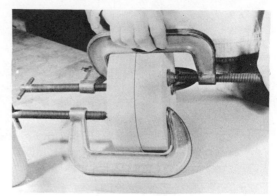

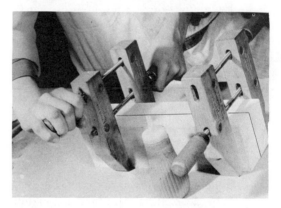

Fig. 2—43 (above). Clamping stock for a turned bowl with C-clamps. Fig. 2—44 (below). Clamping stock for a turned lamp base with hand screws.

Fig. 2—45. Bar clamps hold together a glued table top. Note the use of newspapers to catch drippings.

save hours of work later on. Let the glue dry at least as long as the directions recommend, before removing the clamps.

7. Apply the adhesive to only as many parts as you can quickly clamp together. Modern adhesives set rapidly and if clamping is delayed, maximum strength will not be obtained.

SHARPENING TOOLS

Sharp tools make woodworking fun, easy, quick, and safer. The dull tool produces sloppy work, tries one's patience, and actually causes more injuries than a sharp one. For good craftsmanship it is as necessary to be able to keep a tool sharp as it is to be able to use it skillfully.

The simplest edge to sharpen is the wedge. It can be done with a file, stone, or on the side of a grinding wheel. It is preferred on tools that are given hard usage, such as hatchets, axes, rough knives, and auger bits.

Hollow ground edges are the sharpest, but because they are thin they dull easily, for example, a razor blade. Hollow grinding is done on the rim of the grinding wheel. A large diameter wheel produces a nearly flat edge, while a small wheel grinds a distinctly hollow edge. For most woodworking tools, a 6″ wheel is recommended.

How to Hollow Grind an Edge:

1. Grind only when the edge is chipped or worn away. It is not necessary to grind the edge each time the tool is dull; honing alone is usually sufficient.

2. Use a guide to support the tool at the desired angle. If the grinder does not have a special tool holder, use

TYPES OF CUTTING EDGES

DOUBLE BEVEL

A STURDY EDGE FOR ROUGH KNIVES, HATCHETS, ETC.

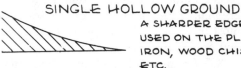

SINGLE HOLLOW GROUND

A SHARPER EDGE USED ON THE PLANE IRON, WOOD CHISEL, ETC.

DOUBLE HOLLOW GROUND

THE SHARPEST EDGE USED ON KNIVES, RAZOR BLADES, ETC.

Fig. 2—46. Types of cutting edges for tools.

the thumb and the forefinger. Grip the blade so that the finger slides along the rest. Do not remove the fingers until the edge is completed.

3. The grinding wheel should turn *into* the edge, not away from it, in order to prevent a wire edge.

4. Use a medium or coarse wheel for the rough grinding. A fine wheel cuts slowly and may burn the edge as you apply pressure. However, it should follow the rough wheel to remove the heavy grinding marks.

5. Use only enough pressure to keep the edge in contact with the wheel, not enough to cause excessive heating. A burned edge turns blue and will have to be ground off because it will not hold its sharpness. Cool the edge frequently with water if it gets too hot to hold.

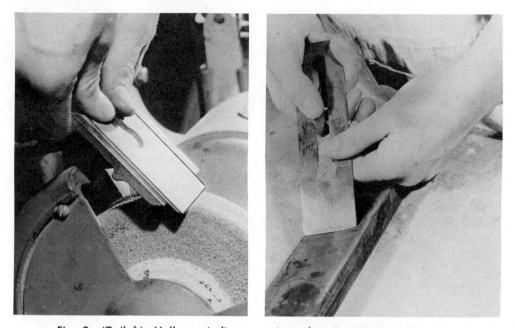

Fig. 2—47 (left). Hollow grinding a cutting edge. Fig. 2—48 (right). Whetting the ground edge on a stone to make a fine, sharp cutting edge.

Whetting and Honing. Whetting is the second step in sharpening. Also called honing, it removes the marks left by the grinding wheel; when done on successively finer stones, a fine, smooth, sharp edge results. The ground edge is held flat against the stone and with a firm, slow motion it is pulled and pushed across the many tiny cutting edges of the abrasive stone. Use a figure "8" motion for an easy rhythmic swing to the honing. A thin oil is needed as a lubricant on the stone to produce a finer cutting edge and to help keep the removed particles from clogging the stone. Whetting is done several times between grindings, as many as 10 or 12, depending on the usage.

Start on the medium grade hone and after a few strokes advance to the next finer.

Stropping. Just as a barber strops his razor on a leather strop to draw out the sharpest edge, so will stropping a hollow ground tool edge provide the finishing touch to sharpening. Instead of pushing the edge into the strop as in honing, pull it away or else you will cut the strop into two pieces.

Sharpening a Plane Iron. Follow the procedure just described, for sharpening the plane iron. The width of the bevel should be about 1½ times the thickness of the iron.

Sharpening Chisels and Gouges. The wood chisel is sharpened in very much the same way as the plane iron. The width of the bevel varies from 1 to 1½ times the thickness of the blade. Gouges are also hollow ground. They are honed with a slipstone—a tapered stone with round edges.

Sharpening an Auger Bit. A special auger bit file is used for sharpening the cutting edges of an auger bit. The lips are filed on the top side only, and the spurs on the inside only. The spurs cut the rim of the hole; the lips cut away the inside.

Sharpening Twist Drill Bits. Sharpening twist drills, especially the small sizes that are most used in woodworking, requires precision grinding. When new they are sharpened to cut several materials, including metals. If they are to be sharpened for use in wood only, some changes can be made. The angle including the two cutting lips can be lessened, thus bringing them to more of a point. The cutting edges can be ground with greater clearance to permit thicker shavings. This is preferably done on a drill grinding attachment for the tool grinder.

Saw Sharpening. Saw sharpening involves more than a sharpening of the teeth. The points are all brought to the same height by jointing; and, by *setting*, the teeth are bent alternately left and right to give clearance for the blade as the saw moves through the wood. This procedure is essentially the same for all wood cutting saws, whether they are hand saws or machine. It is important that each tooth do its full share of the work. Consequently it is recommended that saws be sharpened by an expert, or by a machine.

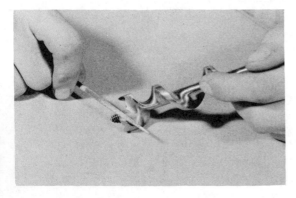

Fig. 2—49 (above). Sharpening an auger bit with a special file. Fig. 2—50 (below). Twist drill bits must be sharpened on a tool grinder.

Courtesy Foley Manufacturing Company

Fig. 2—51. An automatic saw sharpener uses files.

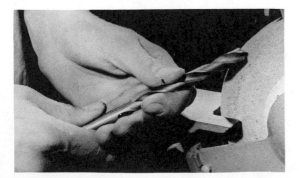

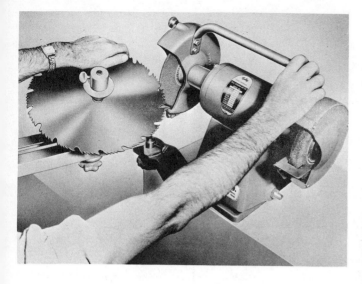

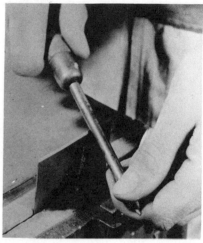

Fig. 2—52. Circular saws are sharpened by grinding or filing.

Fig. 2—53. Rolling the edge of a ▶ scraper with the burnisher to form the burr which does the cutting.

How to Sharpen Scraper Blades:

The woodworker will usually sharpen his own scraper blades, since it must be done frequently. Follow these suggestions:

1. Draw file the edge square; round the two corners slightly.
2. Whet the edge square on a stone, and then whet the flat sides with a few strokes to remove any burrs left by the file.
3. Roll the cutting edges with a *burnisher*. To do this, clamp the blade in a vise so that about 1½″ extend. Hold the burnisher at about 85 degrees to the edge and, pressing it firmly, draw it across the full length of the blade in one stroke. With sufficient pressure this should draw out a cutting edge. Repeat on the other side.
4. To test for a burr cutting edge, slide your fingers toward the blade and over the burr. If you cannot feel it, it isn't there. You may have only rounded the edge. This means that the entire process must be repeated beginning with the filing.
5. This drawn edge is delicate and wears down quickly on hard wood, but it does an excellent job of smoothing on the most stubborn grain.

A bevel edge scraper blade is sharpened in the same way, except that the edge is filed at 45 degrees and only the sharp edge is rolled with the burnisher.

Testing for Sharpness. The final test of sharpness is in the cutting. However, an edge tool when moved slowly across one's fingernail with no pressure other than the weight of the blade, if sharp, will *drag* on the nail and make a slight scratch. If dull, it will skid.

SOME STEPS TO REMEMBER IN SMOOTHING WOOD:

It is usually best to do the smoothing of parts before assembly. After assembly only a light sanding is necessary before finishing.

The Faces:
1. Plane by hand or machine, if necessary.
2. Scrape, if needed, to smooth chipped areas.
3. Swell out any dents. A drop of water on a dent causes the fibers to swell. A damp pad laid over the depression and heated with an electric iron steams it out.
4. Sand with a medium or finer abrasive.
5. Sand with a fine abrasive before assembly.

The Edges:
1. Joint (true) with hand plane or jointer.
2. If an edge is to be glued to another, do not sand.
3. If the edge is to be exposed, remove the sharpness with a block plane or sandpaper.

The Ends:
1. Cut accurately with back saw or power saw.
2. If the end is to be exposed, sand first with medium abrasive and then with fine.
3. If the end is to be fitted, as in a butt joint, do not sand. Sanding rounds edges and destroys the accuracy of the fit.

After assembly, wipe the surfaces with a damp sponge. When dry, the grains will be raised and rough. Do the final sanding with very fine abrasive.

FOR RESEARCH, EXPERIMENT, DEVELOPMENT

1. How does one find the diameter of a piece already cut round?
2. Why is a pencil preferred to a scriber for marking on wood?
3. Why can a board be cut off more easily with a crosscut saw than with a rip saw?
4. Why is it more difficult to cut straight lines with a coping saw than with a back saw?
5. Why is a dull tool often more dangerous than a sharp one?
6. Why does a drill bit get hot when drilling in wood?
7. Why should clamps be used when gluing?
8. How should a knife be ground to make the sharpest edge?
9. Why does honing sharpen even a newly ground edge?
10. What advantages, if any, do hand methods have over machine methods?

chapter 3

MACHINE TOOLS

Machines are intended to produce a high degree of accuracy more quickly than is possible by hand methods. Machine tools are those tools that have been adapted to machine power and speeds. For example, the portable electric drill is a motorized version of the hand drill, and easily out-performs the hand drill. The drill press adds features to the electric drill that provide greater precision and operator control. These make the drill press suitable for the identical processing of quantities of parts.

Different types of skills are required for operating machine tools than for hand tools. Any hand tool requires muscle power; the machine tool requires little, if any. There are certain qualifications, however, that one must have to use machine tools wisely and well. The operator must be mature—"grown-up"— enough to realize that instruction is necessary and that study of the machine is essential. He must be intelligent enough to know that the machine does not think; he must provide that. He must have presence of mind in order to insure safe, positive, accurate control of the machine at all times. "Scatter-brains" and "wise-guys" are not competent to operate machines without danger to themselves and to others. If your teacher does not permit you to use a machine, perhaps he is not sure that you can assume responsibility safely. It is up to you to prove to him that you can think and act sanely and safely in all situations.

SOME GENERAL SUGGESTIONS ON THE OPERATION OF WOODWORKING EQUIPMENT

1. It makes good sense to find out as much as possible about the operation of a machine before trying it yourself. Watch the demonstration closely, ask questions, and ask your instructor to check you out each time you try a new machine or make a new setup.

2. Because the same cut may be made on two or more machines, use the best, easiest, and safest one—the proper one, in other words.

3. On any combination machine only one operation should be going on at one time.

4. No cutting tool is likely to jump out and injure you unless it comes loose. Be sure to check the cutting tool frequently.

5. Never leave a machine while the motor is running, not even for a few seconds. Someone else may not see that it is running and could be injured.

6. Some machines require frequent lubrication. Check with your instructor to see if you should look after this.

7. All electric motor driven machines should be grounded. This is important on portable electric tools, too. Clamp the third wire to the conduit unless it has a three-pronged plug.

8. As you become accustomed to us-ing each machine, its sound will become familiar to you. Should you ever hear a strange sound in the machine you are using, shut off the motor.

9. Find out the working principles for each machine and the mechanisms involved. This will help you to use the machines more masterfully, and you will be better able to help with their maintenance.

10. Do not wear loose-fitting clothing in the shop. Take off your coat and tie, put on an apron, roll up your sleeves and you are in the proper mood and attire to get some good work done. And incidentally, this makes safety sense, too.

THE JIG SAW

The jig saw, or scroll saw, resembles a power-driven coping saw. The short blade moves up and down, cutting only on the down stroke. The saw is designed especially for cutting fine curves and de-

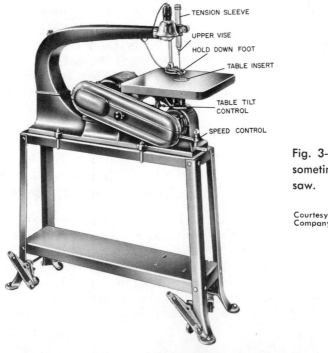

TENSION SLEEVE
UPPER VISE
HOLD DOWN FOOT
TABLE INSERT
TABLE TILT CONTROL
SPEED CONTROL

Fig. 3—1. The jig saw is sometimes called a scroll saw.

Courtesy Rockwell Manufacturing Company

tails in stock up to approximately an inch in thickness. With a tilting table, it can make angular cuts. A built-in blower clears the sawdust from in front of the blade.

Limitations. The jig saw is probably the most overburdened machine tool in the school shop. It is not intended for heavy cutting; that is for the band saw. It is designed for cutting curves, not straight lines; use the circular saw for straight cutting. It cannot do every job that a coping saw can. It does not cut as fast as a band saw, so take your time. The longer you can saw without breaking a blade, the more expert you are.

Cutting Speeds. The jig saw blade cuts best when run at the proper speed for wood. When it is too slow, the tendency is to feed the material too fast, to force the cutting. Fast speeds cut best, but require more skill in directing the material. Feed the wood only as fast as you can control the direction of the cutting. The speed is adjusted by either shifting the belt or adjusting the speed control. The middle speeds are best for cutting wood.

Jig Saw Blades. Jig saw blades are usually 5″ in length and are available in various combinations of widths and teeth per inch (tpi). The blade is selected according to the kind of sawing. The thinner the wood, the more teeth per inch; the sharper the curves, the narrower the blade. A blade about 0.110-inch wide and 8 or 10 tpi serves for general cutting.

How to Install a Blade:
1. Remove the table insert and loosen the upper and lower blade vises. Slip the blade into the lower vise and then into the upper, with the teeth pointing down. Tighten each vise with the thumb screw; pliers should not be

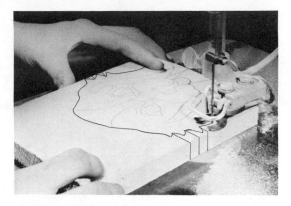

Fig. 3—2. Guide the work with both hands and feed it into the jig saw blade just fast enough to keep it cutting. Note the preliminary cuts from edge to mark, at points of sharp change in direction.

necessary. There should not be less than a half-inch of blade in each vise.

2. Turn the motor over slowly by hand to see if the blade is correctly tensioned. If it bends, the upper spring housing must be raised to add tension and to clear the upper vise. The housing must clear the vise at the top of the stroke.

3. Check the blade guide. It should be wide enough to provide a free fit and should not be set so deep as to touch the blade teeth. The blade support, a roller, should barely turn when the blade is moving but not cutting.

Plan for Sawing. To speed up sawing and to prevent the blade from getting so far into the stock that it can not be backed out, make a plan for your sawing. First make the cuts into the centers of the curves and to the bottoms of the V's. Then saw around the outline and the pieces will fall away.

Courtesy Rockwell Manufacturing Company

Fig. 3—3. For cutting out holes, the jig saw blade is installed through a hole bored in the waste stock.

How to Jig Saw:
1. Check for the proper blade speed.
2. Adjust the hold-down fingers to press lightly on the work.
3. Guide the work with both hands when the piece is large enough so that the fingers are not in the way of the blade.
4. Push the work into the blade just fast enough to keep it cutting. When making sharp turns, be sure to keep the blade cutting or it will break.
5. To cut out holes, drill a hole large enough to admit the blade, near the line in the waste stock, and install the blade through it.
6. Should the blade break in sawing, and this can happen either from fatigue or misuse, stop the motor.

☞ **SAFETY SENSE**

The jig saw is as safe as a machine tool can be, but carelessness can make it cruel.

1. Keep your fingers to the side of the blade, never in front of it.
2. Use as slow a blade speed as is consistent with good cutting until you have acquired skill and confidence in yourself.
3. The light should shine on the cutting, not in your eyes.
4. Shut off the motor when the sawing is complete or when you leave the machine.

THE BAND SAW

The band saw is a most versatile machine. It has an endless blade traveling around two wheels like a flat belt around two pulleys. The blade travels so that the cut is continuous and downward against the table. It cuts curves and straight lines in thin as well as in thick stock. Some band saws will cut stock 6″, 8″ or more in thickness. They cut much faster than a jig saw but are less suitable for the fine details. With a fence the band saw can be used for ripping and resawing (cutting a board into thinner boards).

The size of the band saw is given in inches, as 12″, 18″, or other. This means that a 12-inch band saw, for example, will cut to the center of a 24-inch circle. Saws operating on the same principle are used in lumber mills for ripping logs; they may have blades a foot wide.

Blades. Blades come in various widths and with different numbers of teeth per inch. In general, use a blade as wide as possible and with as few teeth as the stock will allow. The thinner the material, the more teeth needed. But fine teeth cut heavy stock too slowly, and the extra friction may cause the blade to overheat. Blade speed is usually fixed, and it is not necessary to change it on a wood-cutting band saw.

Limitations. Only the uninformed person will overload any machine, or use it for purposes for which it was not intended. In the case of the band saw, when sharp curves are to be cut, install a narrow blade. A wide blade binds on sharp curves and may snap in two. For example, a ¼″ blade will cut curves of 1″ radius and larger, but has difficulty with smaller ones. Heavy sawing can overload the blade. Although it may handle 6″ balsa easily, it may not cut more than 3″ maple, and this, very slowly.

How to Install a Blade:

1. Remove both wheel guards. Release the blade tension by turning the con-

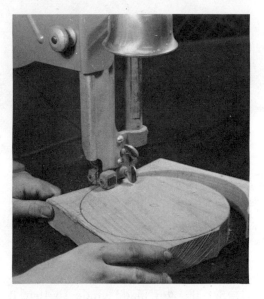

Fig. 3—5. The band saw cuts curves in heavy stock.

trol knob on the back of the upper wheel frame. Remove the table insert and slide the blade out.

2. Replace the new blade, centering it on the wheel rims. Put a slight tension on it and turn the wheels by hand to align the tracking of the blade. The band must run centered on the rims. If it tends to run off, adjust the tracking device located near the tension control.

3. Possibly the upper and lower blade guides will have to be moved. When the blade tracks accurately, increase the tension on the blade until it is taut, but still has some "give" when pressed with a finger. Now adjust the blade guides so that they just clear the teeth. Move the thrust wheels up to the back of the blade. The wheels should barely turn when no pressure is applied to the blade while sawing.

Fig. 3—4. The band saw and its parts.

Courtesy Rockwell Manufacturing Company

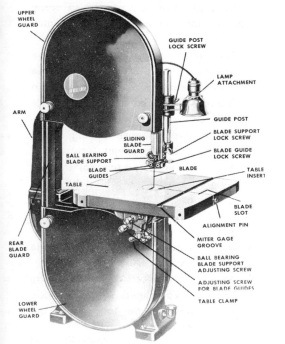

UPPER WHEEL GUARD

GUIDE POST LOCK SCREW

LAMP ATTACHMENT

ARM

GUIDE POST

BLADE SUPPORT LOCK SCREW

SLIDING BLADE GUARD

BLADE GUIDE LOCK SCREW

BALL BEARING BLADE SUPPORT

BLADE GUIDES

BLADE

TABLE INSERT

TABLE

BLADE SLOT

ALIGNMENT PIN

MITER GAGE GROOVE

REAR BLADE GUARD

BALL BEARING BLADE SUPPORT ADJUSTING SCREW

ADJUSTING SCREW FOR BLADE GUIDES

TABLE CLAMP

LOWER WHEEL GUARD

Fig. 3—6. Ripping with the aid of the fence on a band saw.

Courtesy Rockwell Manufacturing Company

How to Operate the Band Saw:

1. Set the top blade guide so that it clears the stock by about a half inch. Turn on the motor and let the machine run for a few seconds to see that the blade is properly tracking.
2. Lay the work on the table and holding it with both hands, feed it slowly into the blade.
3. Cut on the outside of the line, using just enough pressure to keep the blade cutting at all times. To keep from binding, the blade must be cutting as it turns a curve.
4. Follow a cutting plan for intricate work, just as on the jig saw, so that you don't have to back the blade out of a cut. It can be easily pulled off the wheels when backing out.

Crosscutting. The miter gauge is used for crosscutting just as is done on the table saw.

Ripping. This is done with the fence, as on the table saw (see p. 43–44).

Re-sawing. Wide stock should be sawed as deeply as possible from both edges on the table saw. Then the center is sawed on the band saw, using the fence. For accurate cutting, use a wide band saw blade.

Bevel-cutting. The table is tilted to the desired angle for cutting bevels. Special attention must be given to safety because of the inconvenient position of the stock.

☞ **SAFETY SENSE**

A band saw cuts so fast and so easily that the operator must constantly watch his fingers.

1. Use only a sharp blade. A dull one will soon break. Blade fatigue is the common cause of breakage. When a blade does break, shut off the motor at once.
2. To observe someone sawing, stand behind and to the right.
3. Keep the light focused not in your eyes but on the spot where the blade is cutting.
4. Keep your fingers to the side of the blade; never in front of it.
5. Make no adjustments while the blade is running.
6. Shut off the motor as soon as the sawing is completed. Drop the blade guide down to the table when the blade has stopped.
7. Leave wood scraps on the table until the blade has stopped.

THE CIRCULAR SAW

The circular saw, also called the bench or table saw, is one of the basic machines for woodworking. On it the following processes may be performed: crosscutting, ripping, mitering, beveling, chamfering, rabbeting, and with attachments, cove cutting, tapering, dadoing, sanding, shaping, and molding cutting. This machine, although very commonplace, demands the complete respect of anyone who operates it. Whenever one ignores this demand, he, rather than the saw, is likely to be the cause of an injury. This respect includes the understanding of what can be done and what should not be attempted on the machine.

Fig. 3—7 (above). Re-sawing to thinner stock using the band saw. Fig. 3—8 (below). The circular saw.

Both photographs courtesy Rockwell Manufacturing Company

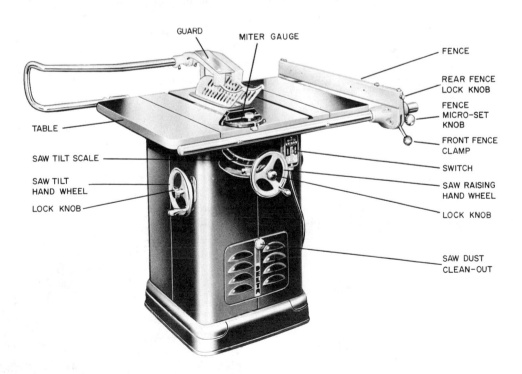

There are two basic types of circular saws, the tilting table and the tilting arbor. For making certain angular cuts, either the table or the blade must tilt. The tilting arbor is recommended for accuracy, convenience, and safety. Sizes of circular saws are given as the diameter of the blade; for example, an 8″, 10″, or 12″.

Types of Saw Blades. Blades are designed for specific cuts, such as rip, crosscut, and planer. Combination blades are general purpose saws. The rip blade is effective only for ripping, just as the crosscut is only for cutting across the grain. They are not interchangeable. The planer blade is hollow ground and is used only for making very accurate cuts in joinery. The combination blade does both crosscutting and ripping satis-

factorily. Some saw blades are made with tungsten carbide tips brazed on. Such teeth stay sharp and hold their cutting edges longest.

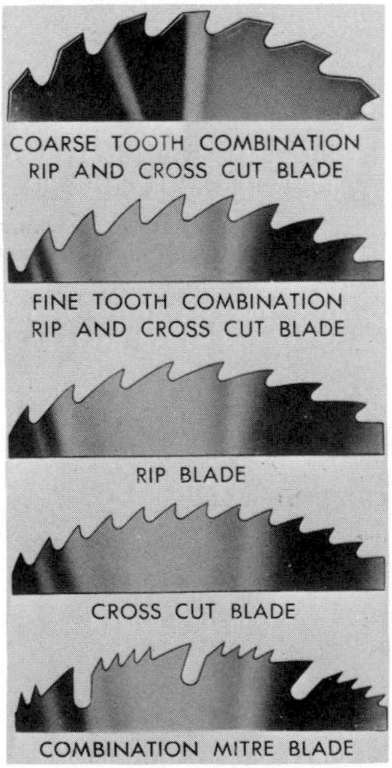

The Guard. The saw guard is intended to make accidents less likely, but it is not completely foolproof. Present guards cannot be used for all types of cuts; however, the guard should always be in place when it can be used, as well as when the saw is not in use. There is a legal point which holds that if a machine cannot be operated with a guard, it should not be operated. If this were the practice perhaps more effective guards would be devised. A good guard has an anti-kickback device to prevent the blade from throwing the work back at the operator. It has a splitter which holds the kerf open, thus keeping the stock from binding the blade. The kerf is the cut made through the wood. This is especially important while ripping.

How to Crosscut:

1. Remove the fence and adjust the height of the blade so that it will just cut through the stock. Put the miter

Fig. 3—9. Types of circular saw blades.

Courtesy Stanley Electric Tools

COARSE TOOTH COMBINATION
RIP AND CROSS CUT BLADE

FINE TOOTH COMBINATION
RIP AND CROSS CUT BLADE

RIP BLADE

CROSS CUT BLADE

COMBINATION MITRE BLADE

Fig. 3—10. The anti-kickback fingers and the splitter in position. The guard over the blade has been removed to show these features.

Courtesy Rockwell Manufacturing Company

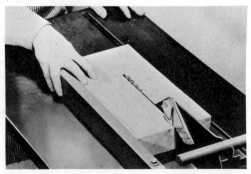

Fig. 3—11. Crosscutting narrow stock, with the stock ahead of the miter gauge.
Fig. 3—12. Crosscutting wide stock with the guard removed to show the setup.

gauge in the left table groove, unless the right is more convenient.

2. Place the board against the gauge and align the cut-off mark with the blade. Be sure to allow for the kerf.
3. With the guard in position turn on the motor, hold the work snugly and securely against the gauge, and push the board slowly into the saw and then on past it so that it is completely cut.
4. Keeping one hand on the work, shut off the motor. Wait until the saw stops before removing the pieces. Never try to hold both pieces. If one is too long to stay on the table, get a buddy to hold the end. If the board is as much as 6′ long, it is a good idea to first cut it in two with a hand saw.

How to Rip:

1. Remove the miter gauge and hang it up. Each time it falls to the floor it loses some of its accuracy. Set the blade to just clear the stock.
2. Move the fence into position, using the scale on the front guide bar, or measure from the fence to the nearest saw tooth. Lock the fence, and position the guard.

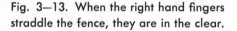

Fig. 3—13. When the right hand fingers straddle the fence, they are in the clear.

Fig. 3—14. Use a push stick when ripping narrow stock.

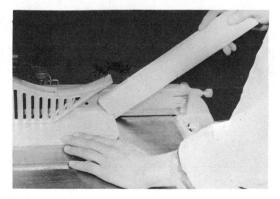

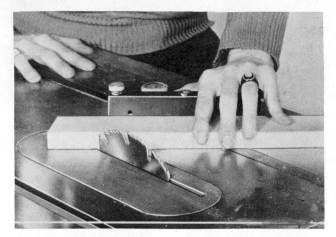

Fig. 3—15. Mitering with the miter gauge. The guard has been removed to show the setup.

Courtesy Rockwell Manufacturing Company

3. Start the motor and, holding the stock against the fence, push it slowly and steadily into the blade. Use the push stick when the stock is too narrow to hold safely by hand.

4. Push the board past the saw and, if it is especially long, have your buddy catch the pieces as they extend from the rear of the table. Turn off the motor.

Fig. 3—16. Four methods for cutting pieces to the same length. The guard has been removed to show the setup.

Courtesy Rockwell Manufacturing Company

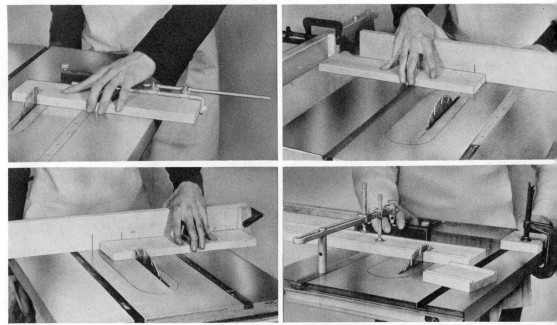

Mitering. Miter joints are cut in the same way as crosscutting. The miter gauge must be set at the desired angle. Use it in either table groove, but make sure it will clear the blade. Make test cuts in scrap stock to check on the accuracy of the joint. There is a tendency for a board to creep into the blade and change the angle. Either hold the stock firmly and feed it slowly, or clamp it to the miter gauge.

Cutting to Length. When several pieces are to be cut to the same length, it is necessary to use some type of guide. The stop rod that is a part of the miter gauge is the handiest. A block can also be clamped to the fence ahead of the blade. Set the desired length from the block to the saw cut and lock the fence. The block provides clearance so that the piece being cut will not bind between the blade and the fence.

Beveling and Chamfering. Beveling is done with the aid of either the miter gauge or the fence, depending on the direction of the grain of wood. The saw blade is tilted to the desired angle. Chamfering is done similarly, except that less stock is removed.

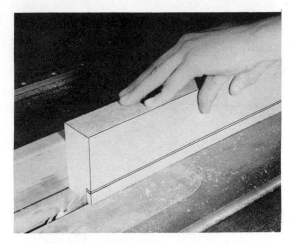

Fig. 3—18. Many cuts can be made only with the guard removed, as shown in this illustration. This may present a hazard. Check first with your teacher.

Rabbeting. To cut a rabbet, the guard must be removed. Make sure, first of all, that you have the instructor's permission to do this. Set the blade for the desired depth and the fence for the desired width. Two cuts are necessary; make the edge cut first.

Tenoning. Freehand cutting of tenons is not recommended, especially when the piece is long and must be held vertically. A tenoning jig makes the cutting easier and safer. Make the shoulder crosscuts with the miter gauge and the cheek cuts with the jig (see Fig. 3-19).

Cove Cutting. This cut is especially interesting to watch because one is not likely to believe it can be done until he sees it. For a guide, clamp a straight board to the table and at an angle to the blade. With a series of light cuts push the stock along the guide and the saw will cut a concave surface. The angle of the guide is determined by trial (see Fig. 3-20).

Fig. 3—17. Cutting a bevel. The blade is tilted to the desired angle.

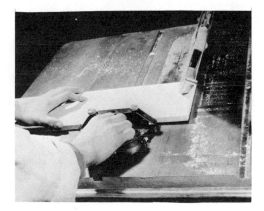

Fig. 3—19 (above). Cutting a tenon with a tenoning jig. Fig. 3—20 (right). Cove cutting.

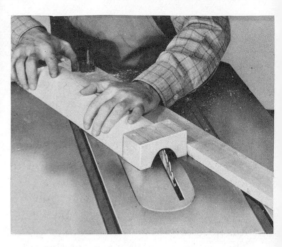

Fig. 3—21. A simple jig attachment for tapering on the circular saw. The guard has been removed to show details.

Fig. 3—22 (left). Cutting a dado with the aid of the miter gauge. Fig. 3—23 (right). A dado head, a dado blade, and the chippers.

Tapering. With the aid of an attachment, tapers can be cut on the circular saw. Mark out the taper on the stock. In the case of square taper legs, mark one leg only. Set the blade to the proper depth as for ripping. Adjust the attachment so that the mark on the stock is parallel to the fence. Make a test cut in the waste stock. Then make the final adjustment. The first pair of adjacent cuts on a leg are made with the same setup. The next pair requires twice as much set over because of the wood already removed.

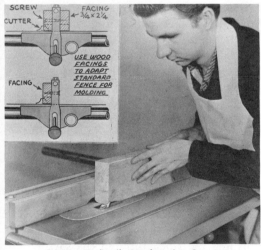

Courtesy Rockwell Manufacturing Company

Fig. 3—24. Shaping an edge with the molding head. This requires removal of the guard—see your instructor first.

The Dado Head. The dado head is a special saw assembly which makes cuts of several widths. It speeds up the cutting of dados, grooves, and rabbets. It is also useful in tenoning. The head consists of two saw blades as outside cutters and a series of inside cutters.

When only one of the outside cutters is used, the groove is usually ⅛″ wide.

In assembling the cutters, the swaged tips of the teeth on the inside cutters must fit into the gullets of the outside cutters. Gullets are the deep valleys between groups of teeth or between teeth. A special dado table insert is used to allow for the thickness of the head. In operation, the cutter is used with either the miter gauge or the fence.

The Molding Head. The molding head is a device for cutting moldings on the edges of boards, table edging, picture framing, and the like. Replaceable knives in the cutter head make many different shapes. A special table insert and fence are necessary. The cut can usually be made in one pass through the head.

👉 **SAFETY SENSE**

1. Always have your teacher check your saw setup before you make a cut until he tells you that you are able to do it properly by yourself.

2. If the blade is dull, replace it with a sharp one. A dull blade burns easily, and excessive pressure is required to force the wood through it. It may bind and throw the piece backwards.

3. Always stand to one side of the blade, never in line with it.

4. When making an adjustment, be sure to stop the machine first.

5. Leave the pieces of wood on the table until the saw stops.

6. The guard should be in place at all times. Get your instructor's permission before removing it.

7. Only your instructor should be standing near you as you operate the machine, unless you have a buddy

of whom your instructor approves. No one should talk to you, nor should you talk to any one.

8. If something seems to be wrong, shut the motor off immediately, but keep hold of the piece.

9. You must keep a secure hold of the stock at all times to overcome the push of the saw. Hold onto the work as long as the saw is turning.

10. Keep the floor in front of the machine clean of sawdust. Sawdust is slippery on a smooth floor. A rubber floor mat is a sensible safety feature which also protects a miter gauge if it is dropped.

11. Use a buddy system for machine operation. Your buddy can check on your machine setup as well as your operation of a machine.

12. Make sure that your setup is such that a piece of stock cannot become wedged between the blade and the fence. If you are not 100% positive that your setup is correct, check with your teacher.

13. When your instructor operates the saw or any machine, it looks so easy. Don't be fooled by this. You may think you know how to use a machine or tool before you really do. Remember, the saw doesn't select what it cuts. You do.

14. When you can figure out the reasons behind each of these safety suggestions, you will have considerable respect for the circular saw.

THE RADIAL SAW

The radial saw is an upside-down saw. The motor and blade are suspended above the work rather than below it. In this position the blade can be raised, lowered, turned, and tilted to make an assortment of cuts. The actual operation of the saw is done with one hand by gently pulling and pushing the motor through the work, using a convenient handle. The direction of the cutting is such that the blade helps to feed itself and little effort is required by the operator.

Numerous attachments are used on the radial saw, including the dado head, shaper, sander, drill, saber saw, and even a wood lathe.

The instructions and information given for the circular saw are in general applicable to this machine.

Adjustments. There are three primary adjustments to be made on the radial saw. *Depth of cut* is determined by raising or lowering the arm at the shoulder, or column. The *direction* of the cut is set at the elbow, where the motor can swivel a complete 360 degrees to crosscut, rip, and miter. Settings for *bevel* cuts are made at the wrist, where the motor and blade tilt to any angle.

Unlike the circular saw, the stock used with the radial saw remains stationary on the table. This makes the radial saw especially convenient for certain cuts. Ripping is done in the usual manner: by pushing the stock through the saw.

Sizes of radial saws are given as the diameters of the blades.

☞ **SAFETY SENSE**

To one who is accustomed to the circular saw, the radial saw is a definite departure. The entire mechanism is visible and accessible above the work. The saw blade can be seen as it cuts within its guard. This fact may make the radial saw appear hazardous. The assumption is that since the blade cannot be clearly seen

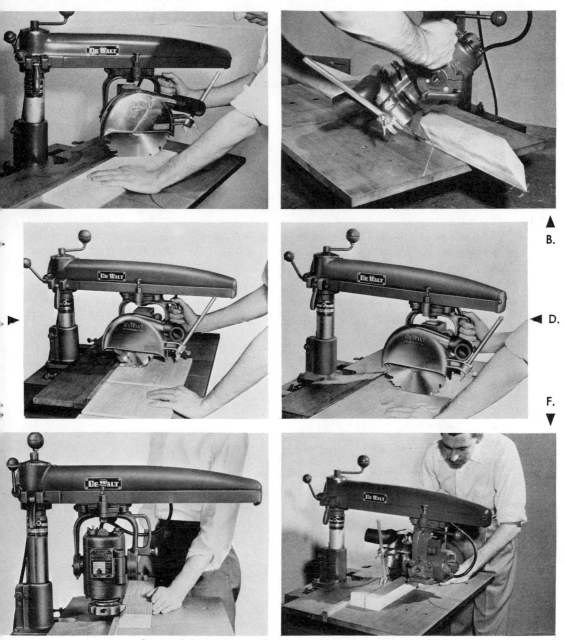

Courtesy DeWalt Incorporated

Fig. 3—25. Using the radial saw for various operations. A. Mitering. B. A bevel-miter on the radial saw. C. Dadoing. D. Cutting off a board. E. A molding head on the radial saw. F. Ripping.

in the bench saw, it must be safer. A comparative study will point out the weaknesses in this assumption.

One item of specific concern with the radial saw, however, is the tendency of the blade to coast for an appreciable time after the motor is shut off. It spins so quietly that it may be unnoticed and offer a chance for an accident. With a magnetic brake this hazard is eliminated. Here are some specific suggestions for safe operation of the radial saw:

1. Do not attempt to stop the saw blade by forcing a piece of wood against it, after the motor is shut off.
2. Do not change a setup until the blade has stopped.
3. Be sure all adjustment clamps are locked before turning on the motor.
4. Keep the material against the fence; when crosscutting, the saw helps to do this.

5. Start a cut only when the motor is back against the column. This may not apply when ripping, however.
6. Make sure the guard is properly positioned.

THE JOINTER

The jointer smooths and straightens faces and edges as you would like a hand plane to be able to do. Sometimes called the jointer-planer, the machine can save hours of work and do more accurate work than the hand plane. This machine can also rabbet, bevel, chamfer, and taper. The working part is the cutter head, usually with three knives, sharpened like plane irons, which turn at speeds of 5,000 rpm or more. With three knives at this speed, a total of 15,000 cuts can be made per minute. Try that on a hand plane. This speed accounts

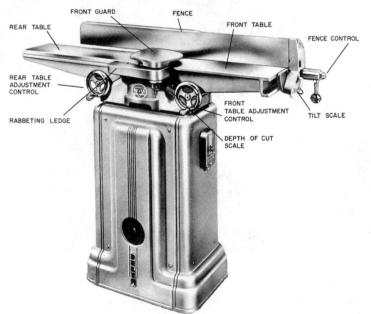

Fig. 3—26. The jointer.

Courtesy Rockwell Manufacturing Company

for the smoothness of the cut. Depth of cut is determined by the table setting. It depends on the type of cut and the kind of wood.

Jointer Knives. When the knives are sharp, the jointer cuts easily, smoothly, and relatively noiselessly. When dull, they resist the board and make an excessive noise as they literally "spank" it. The knives are aligned so that each does an equal share of the cutting. When nicked, they leave a raised bead on the surface of the work.

Replacing knives is a delicate operation. Each is set in place, gently tightened with the set screws, and then adjusted for position. To do that, lay a straight piece of wood about an inch wide and a foot long over the throat at one end of the cutter. Mark the position of the back end of the stick on the table with a pencil. Turn the cutter head until the knife touches the stick,

carries it, and drops it. Then mark the location of the back of the stick again. The idea now is to get each end of each blade to move the stick the same distance. This is done by raising and lowering the blades. Set one knife first, tighten it securely, and then do the others.

Adjusting the Tables. Each table is adjusted up or down by a crank and can be locked in position with a hand screw. The rear table is so set that it is even with the top edge of the blades in their top position. Lay a wooden straight edge on the table and raise or lower it until it just touches the knives. This table is then left in this position and adjustments for depth of cut are made with the front table.

How to Joint an Edge:

1. Set the front table for approximately a ⅟₁₆″ cut. Most tables have fixed stops at 90 degrees. Check the fence however, with a try square for squareness with the tables.
2. With the guard in place, turn on the motor. Place the work on edge on the front table against the fence. Holding the board in position, slide it over and past the cutter until the guard closes behind it.
3. Stand squarely balanced on both feet so that you can conveniently follow through with the board without having to lean awkwardly.
4. One cut may be sufficient. You can see whether or not the cut covers the entire edge. Shut off the motor when the jointing is completed.
5. End grain may be jointed too, but only when the end is at least three times as wide as the throat. Be sure to clear this with your teacher before you try it. End jointing should precede edge jointing to prevent splintering.

Fig. 3—27. Jointing an edge.

Courtesy Rockwell Manufacturing Company

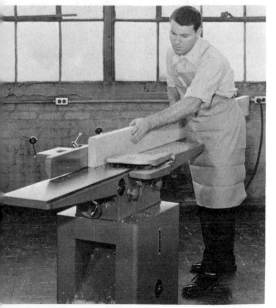

How to Plane a Face:

1. It is recommended that planing be done only on stock that is no wider than the capacity of the jointer. Set the table for a light cut; move the fence, if necessary.

2. Lay the board on the front table, so that the cut will be made *with the grain*. Turn on the motor and slowly push the piece into the cutter. Do not let your leading hand move over the throat with the board. Keep it on your side of the cutter. When 8" or 10" have been planed, move one hand to that end and hold the board in contact with the rear table. Use a *pusher* with the rear hand. This holds the work better and safer than does the hand. Push the stock to clear the throat until the guard returns to position. Repeat the process, if necessary.

Fig. 3—28. Planing a face on the jointer, using the pusher.

Courtesy Rockwell Manufacturing Company

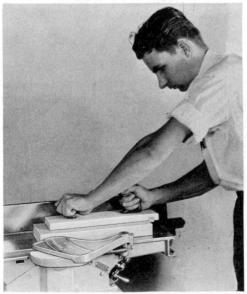

Courtesy Rockwell Manufacturing Company

Fig. 3—29. Cutting a rabbet in a single pass. The guard has been removed to show the setup. Sometimes, however, it is necessary to remove the guard in order to make the cut. Never do this without checking with your instructor.

How to Cut a Rabbet:

1. The rabbeting ledge is at the left side of the front table.

2. Remove the guard and slide the fence over to the ledge at the desired position. The distance from the end of the blades to the fence is the width of the rabbet. The front table is set for the full depth of the cut that is to be made.

3. Feed the board into the cutters slowly, keeping it snug against the tables and fence.

Beveling and Chamfering. The fence is tilted and locked at the desired angle. It is somewhat safer to tilt it toward the table. Operate the machine as for edge jointing.

Planing a Taper on a Jointer:

1. Mark out the taper on the stock.

2. Tack a small block of the thickness of the taper at one end of the stock. This raises the end and permits the opposite end to be cut.

SAFETY SENSE

1. Stock which is shorter than three times the width of the throat should not be run through the jointer.
2. Always use a pusher on short stock and when the material is less than 1" thick. Use it also when jointing a narrow piece.
3. While learning the use of the jointer, take light cuts. They are easily made and require little pressure to be pushed through the cutter.
4. Watch where you put your fingers. So long as they never get over the throat of the machine they cannot be cut. When jointing an edge, keep them high up on the board, and if possible slide them along the top of the fence. Watch the heel of the hand at the end of the board when surfacing.
5. Stand so that you cannot lose your balance as you lean across the tables.

THE PLANER

The planer is the machine that automatically surfaces the stock to thickness. Common sizes are 12", 18", and 24", referring to the width of stock that can be accommodated. Glued-up table tops can be surfaced in the larger machines, saving hours of work with the hand plane. Usually the only adjustment to be made in the operation of the planer is for depth of cut. Light cuts generally produce smoother surfaces than heavy cuts. The stock is fed into the throat of the machine which then takes over and feeds itself as it surfaces. The recommended depth of cut is $\frac{1}{16}$" to $\frac{1}{8}$". When the cut is completed, the stock is released on the opposite side of the machine. Grasp the stock as it leaves the cutter, or the end may receive an extra deep cut as the free end drops.

Well-guarded, the machine is unusually safe to operate, but it is extremely

Fig. 3—30. A planer-surfacer. The table is adjusted up and down for thickness.

Courtesy Yates-American Machine Company

noisy, especially as it becomes dull. When it is running, it is important that operators of other machines double their efforts at concentrating on their own work. Only clean, nail-free lumber should be run through the planer. A nicked blade makes grinding necessary and this involves a major operation.

THE DRILL PRESS

The drill press was originally designed for the accurate, quick drilling of holes, but with the many attachments now available, it can be used for boring, routing, mortising, shaping, sanding, countersinking, and even planing wood. It may be hand- or foot-operated and have one or several spindles which permit boring several holes simultaneously.

Sizes are given as the distance from the center of the drill bit to the post. Speeds can be varied, usually by shifting a belt. The table moves up and down and tilts for angular drilling.

Drill Speeds. Proper drill and feed speeds are important for efficient operation. Three factors must be considered: the density of the wood, the diameter of the hole, and the type of the drill. The harder the wood, the slower the drill speed and the less the feed. The larger the drill bit, the slower the speed of the spindle. When a bit turns too fast, it generates so much heat that it burns and turns blue, becoming useless. No coolants are used. For deep drilling the bit should be lifted frequently to clear out the chips and to permit cooling.

If your drill press has four speeds, the lower two will serve most of your needs.

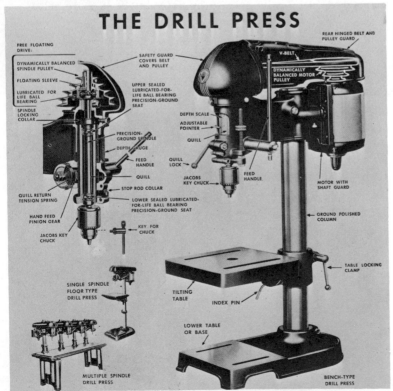

THE DRILL PRESS

Fig. 3–31. The drill press.

Courtesy Rockwell Manufacturing Company

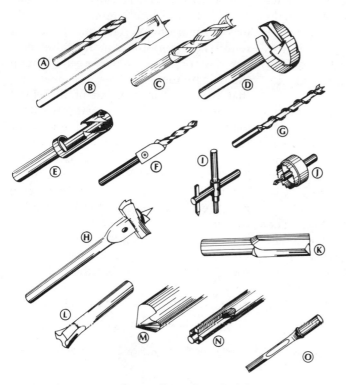

A. twist drill

B. power auger bit

C. spur machine drill

D. multi-spur machine bit

E. plug cutter

F. adjustable countersink attachment

G. solid-center bit

H. expansive bit

I. fly cutter (hole cutter)

J. hole saw

K. router bit

L. dovetail cutter

M. countersink

N. counterbore (with center pilot)

O. hollow chisel

Courtesy Magna Power Tool Corporation

Fig. 3—32. Some bits for use in the drill press. Note that all of the shanks are round. This means that they are intended for use in a drill press or other power drill.

If it has more than four, the middle speeds should usually be used.

Types of Drill Bits. In addition to twist drills (see pp. 24-25), there are Forstner bits, auger bits, spur bits, and hole saws, all of which can be used in the drill press. The twist drill is for holes up to ½". The Forstner bit cuts large holes with flat bottoms. Machine auger bits are similar to the hand type except that they do not have a lead screw. The spur bit is a combination of the auger bit and the twist drill.

Hole saws are used for cutting holes larger than an inch in diameter. This tool has a saw-type blade bent into a circle and clamped in a mandrel. It is chucked in the drill press and should revolve at a slow speed (see item **J** in Fig. 3-32).

How to Drill a Hole:

1. Insert the bit into the chuck and tighten it with a chuck key. Set the proper drill speed.

2. Position the table so that when the drill is at its highest position, the work can be inserted with about ½" clearance. For straight drilling, center the table under the bit. To drill through the work, put a piece of

scrap stock under it. This prevents splintering the underside of the hole and striking the table with the bit.

3. Bring the tip of the bit down to the work at the desired spot, turn on the motor, and press the bit into the wood.

4. When the hole is completed, raise the bit and shut off the motor.

5. The depth gauge on the spindle permits the drilling of holes to uniform depths, or it can be set to prevent boring clear through the stock. Use it whenever you can.

Mortising With the Drill Press. The drill press and a mortising attachment make quick work of cutting accurate mortises, but like all attachments, it requires time to install and to adjust. It is well to plan your work so that all of

your mortising can be done at one time. The hollow chisel mortiser actually makes square holes. The spur bit cuts a round hole and the square chisel cuts out the corners as it is forced through the hole by the feed lever. It is necessary that the bit clear the end of the chisel by about $\frac{1}{16}''$. When the setup has been made, according to the instructions for the attachment, the depth gauge is adjusted and a slow drill speed is selected. The first cut is made slowly, and, when completed, the next one should overlap it. Let each one overlap the last one before it.

Routing and Shaping on the Drill Press. These processes require very high speeds, which means that the drill press must be in first class condition to minimize vibration. The regular chuck can-

Fig. 3—33 (left). Chucking a bit. It is locked with the key. Fig. 3—34 (right). Drilling a hole with a spur bit.

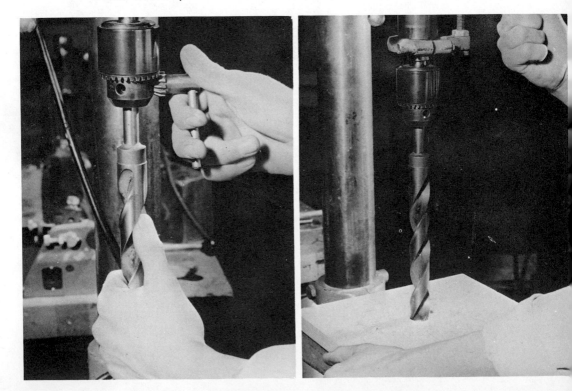

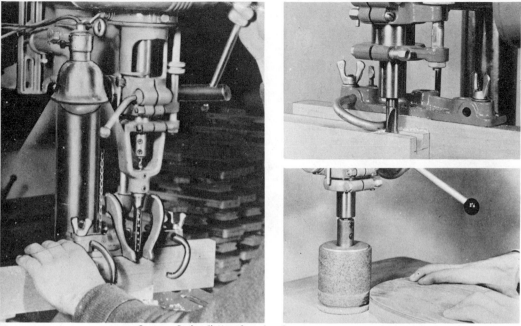

Fig. 3—35 (left). Mortising on the drill press. Fig. 3—36 (right, top). The drill chuck is not used. Fig. 3—37 (right, bottom). Sanding on the drill press.

not be used because it may come loose. A special holder is fastened to the spindle, or a special spindle is used. When the attachments have been installed, the operation is similar to that of the regular router or shaper.

Sanding on the Drill Press. Several sizes of cylindrical, or drum, sanders can be used on the drill press. They may be as small as ½″ in diameter and as large as 5″ or 6″. They use sanding sleeves and are operated at moderate speeds. Disc sanders are also available, but the drum sanders are most suitable for the drill press. They are especially convenient for smoothing inside curves.

Plug Cutting. To cut round wooden plugs for concealing wood screws, select a plug cutter (see Fig. 3-32 Item E) of the same diameter as the counterbore

(see Fig. 6-4). Chuck it in the drill press. With a slow turning speed, press the cutter through a piece of stock until it strikes the scrap block below.

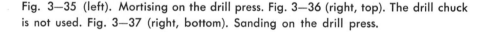 **SAFETY SENSE**

1. The work must always be held securely, either by hand, by clamping to the table, or in a drill press vise.
2. Guards should cover the belts at all times. Use an eye shield for protection against flying chips.
3. Be sure to have your instructor check you out on any attachment you are using for the first time.
4. When a bit squeals, it is rubbing. This probably means that it is dull, full of chips, or that it is not being fed fast enough.

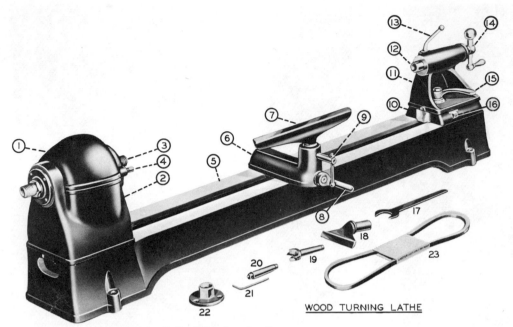

Fig. 3—38. The wood turning lathe. 1. Pulley guard. 2. Headstock. 3. Spindle. 4. Indexing stop. 5. Bed. 6. Tool rest holder. 7. Tool rest. 8. Lock lever. 9. Adjusting screw. 10. Tailstock. 12. Spindle. 13. Spindle lock. 14. Spindle adjusting screw. 15. Tailstock lock. 16. Set-over screw. 17. Headstock wrench. 18. Short tool rest. 19. Spur center. 20. Cup center. 21. Allen wrench. 22. Face plate. 23. Belt.

THE WOOD LATHE

The wood lathe is the machine on which wood is shaped into round and cylindrical shapes, such as bowls, lamps, and table legs. The shaping is done by means of a tool held and manipulated by the operator while the work revolves. The process is called *turning*. Sizes of wood lathes are given as *swing* and the *distance between centers*. A lathe with an 11″ swing will accommodate a piece of stock as large as 11″ in diameter. With 36″ between centers, it will take a piece that long. It is not likely that the lathe will be able to handle a piece 11″ in diameter and 36″ long, however. This would require an extremely heavy duty machine.

Turning Tools. Wood turning tools are shaped to make particular cuts. A dull tool is useless; it makes dust instead of shavings and roughens the surface instead of smoothing it. The tools must be sharpened frequently, especially when used on hard woods. When a tool is burned, nicked, or worn blunt, it must be reground. Between grindings, honing keeps the edge razor sharp. A slip stone and an oil stone are used. The sharper the tool, the easier the turning.

The *round nose* tool is preferably hollow-ground on the bevel as well as on top, as is the *spearpoint*. The gouge is hollow ground on the bevel only. The *parting* tool is hollow ground on both top and bottom. The *skew* chisel is also double hollow ground to a knife-like edge. The *square nose* chisel is hollow ground on the underside, and preferably on top, as is the round nose.

Lathe Speeds. As a rule the faster the wood revolves, the smoother the cut. However, certain speed limitations must be observed in the interests of safety. If the rough stock is not carefully centered and balanced, high speed will throw it out of the lathe. The larger the diameter of the stock, the slower it must revolve. A piece as long as a baseball bat billet should revolve more slowly than a short piece of the same thickness.

When a lathe has several speeds, do the rough cutting on the slowest, then increase the speed one step at a time through the stages of shaping, sanding, and finishing.

Outboard turning on large diameters should be done only when the lathe has extra-slow speeds (see p. 63).

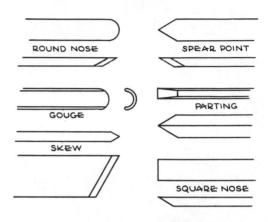

WOOD TURNING TOOLS

ROUND NOSE

SPEAR POINT

GOUGE

PARTING

SKEW

SQUARE NOSE

Fig. 3—39. A set of wood turning tools.

Wood Turning Techniques. There are two basic techniques for turning wood: *scraping* and *cutting*. The first is the simplest. This scraping process involves the holding of the cutting tool squarely on the tool rest and in contact with the wood at the center line. The cutting method requires that the tool be held at

A TABLE OF LATHE SPEEDS
(R. P. M.)

FOR FACE PLATE WORK

Diameter of work	Roughing	Shaping	Sanding	Finishing
3"–4"	500–1000	1000–1500	1500–2000	2000
5"–6"	400–800	800–1200	1200–1500	1500
8"–10"	200–400	300–500	500–700	700

FOR SPINDLE TURNING

1"–2"	500–1000	1000–2000	2000–2500	2500
3"–4"	400–800	800–1200	1200–1500	1500
5"–6"	300–500	500–800	800–1200	1200

an angle to the wood and often above the center, as the cutting edge pares off shavings. The explanations to follow describe the scraping method.

Types of Turning. There are two types of wood turning: *face plate* and *spindle*. Bowls and trays are made on the face plate, while table legs, ball bats, and such are done in spindle turning.

How to Do Face Plate Turning:

1. Get a piece of hard wood, such as cherry or walnut, from which a blank about 2″ thick and 6″ in diameter can be cut. Plane one face true and then cut the blank out on the band saw.
2. Make a full-size drawing of the dish you plan to make. From this make an inside and an outside template (a full-size profile cut from cardboard). Be sure to allow for ¼″ to ⁵⁄₁₆″ thickness at the bottom. The walls need be only ³⁄₁₆″ to ¼″ thick.

Fig. 3–40 (above). Fastening the face plate to the chuck block. Fig. 3–41 (below, left). Rough turning the bowl to true it. Fig. 3–42 (below, right). Hollowing the bowl with the round nose tool.

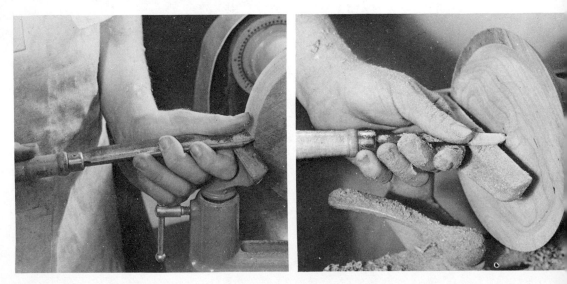

3. Cut out a disc of scrap wood about 1″ thick and about ¼″ smaller in diameter than the foot of the desired bowl. Cut a disc of wrapping paper of the same diameter as the small blank. Now glue this *chuck block* to the smooth side of the bowl blank with the paper in between. Clamp and let dry. The paper in the joint permits easy separation of the bowl from the chuck block when the turning is completed. Have someone hold the finished bowl in his hands while you tap a wide wood chisel into the joint.

4. Fasten the chuck block to the face plate with heavy wood screws, such as ¾-inch No. 12. They should not enter the bowl stock. Screw the face plate securely to the headstock spindle.

5. Set the proper lathe speed. Adjust the tool rest parallel to the edge of the blank at the center line. It

Fig. 3—43. Sanding the inside of the bowl by face plate turning. The tool rest is moved away.

should clear the rest when turned by hand. Screw the tail center against the block.

6. Turn on the motor and hold the gouge firmly in both hands, on the tool rest, and square with the edge of the wood. Slide the tool slowly back and forth across the edge, taking light cuts. Use the forefinger as a guide to follow the tool rest. Move the rest when necessary, keeping it at about ¼″ to ½″ from the work. Stop the machine when making the shift.

7. When the piece is true, the speed may be increased slightly for the shaping. Using a round nose tool, shape the outside, checking progress frequently with the template.

8. Slide the tool rest out of the way when the piece has been shaped. Sand the bowl with 1-0 or finer garnet paper. Keep the abrasive moving from side to side below the center line. Use several thicknesses to prevent burning the fingers. Follow with finer grades until the surface is free of all scratches.

9. To hollow the block, stop the lathe and lock the tool rest across the front, on the center line, and about ⅛″ away. Use the round nose tool again (by this time it probably needs honing). Work from the outside edge to the center of the disc and back. When you go beyond the center, the piece tries to pick up the tool and hand it to you, as if telling you to do it right. Use the template for checking your progress on the inside.

10. Sand the inside as the bowl spins. Do the final sanding with the bowl stopped so that it can be sanded in the direction of the grain.

How to Make a Spindle Turning:

For purposes of illustration, the turning of a baseball bat is described.

1. Make a full-size drawing of the bat to be used.
2. Get the stock, called a *turning square*, or a *billet*, slightly thicker than the greatest diameter of the bat, and about 2″ longer than required.
3. With a back saw make shallow cuts across the corners on each end. This marks the location for the lathe centers. Tap the headstock center into one end of the piece with a mallet. Insert this into the spindle and run the tailstock center into the other end, and draw it up snugly. Turn the piece over by hand a few times to see that it is secure. If it turns loosely, tighten the tailstock.
4. Set the tool rest at the tailstock end to within ¼″ to ⅜″ of the wood and parallel to it on the center line. Turn the stock over by hand to make sure it clears the tool rest. Use the slowest lathe speed.
5. Rough turn a section at a time to make it round, with a heavy gouge,

Fig. 3—44 (left, top). Inserting the ball-bearing tail center. Fig. 3—45 (right, top). Rough turning a ball bat with a gouge. Fig. 3—46. Cutting to diameter with the parting tool, checked with a caliper. Fig. 3—47. Roughing out the shape, guided by the depth cuts.

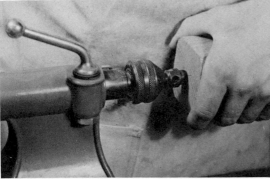

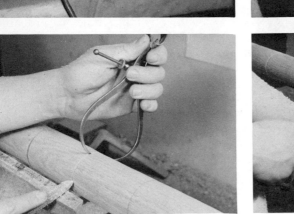

using it as you did for the bowl. When the stock is round, mark out the stations on it according to the drawing. Set a pair of outside calipers to the diameter of the first station plus about ⅟₁₆-inch. Holding the parting tool horizontally and square with the stock, cut into this diameter. Repeat at each station, including the ends. Now cut away the waste stock with the gouge to rough out the shape. The taper is smoothed with a skew chisel or a square nose. Use a round nose to smooth any curves.

6. Sand the bat smooth, using a half sheet of 1-0 garnet paper. Hold the paper by the ends and work it up and down and back and forth over the stock.

7. With the square nose or the parting tool, carefully cut the stub on each end down to about ½-inch diameter. Stop the lathe and, with a back saw, cut off the stubs flush with the ends.

Outboard Turning. Some lathes are equipped for face plate turning on the outside, or outboard, end of the headstock. This is called *outboard turning*. It permits the shaping of larger diameters than could be worked between the two spindles. A special face plate and tool rest are used. The latter is usually mounted on a floor stand. The processes of cutting and smoothing are the same as for inboard turning. But the speed is critical: too much speed causes the entire machine to vibrate excessively. It may even cause the stock to fly apart. Unless the lathe has provision for extra slow speeds, it should not be used for large diameter turning. A piece 18″ to 24″ in diameter should not turn faster than 100 to 150 rpm. Even at this slow speed you will note that the rim is travelling fast. How can one calculate the rim speed?

Finishing on the Lathe. There are wood finishes that can be applied while the piece is in the lathe.

1. For a wax finish, use a pad of soft cloth. Put some paste polishing wax inside of it and hold the pad against the revolving piece. Polish each coat with a soft cloth before applying another. A dozen coats will give a nice soft finish on close-grained wood.

Old-time cabinet makers applied beeswax in a similar manner. A block of wax was held against the surface;

Fig. 3—48. Hollowing a large bowl on the outboard end of a wood lathe.

Courtesy Rockwell Manufacturing Company

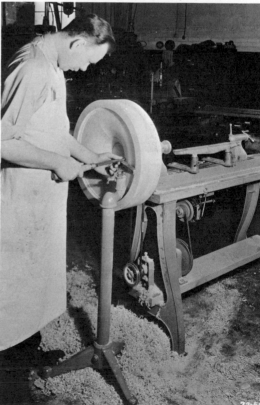

the heat of friction melted it. The surface was burnished with a heavy pad.

2. French polish is the wood turner's favorite. On a pad of cloth lay a teaspoonful of white shellac. Over this place four or five drops of boiled linseed oil. Using moderate pressure, apply this to the surface of the spinning work. When the pad gets dry, repeat the application until a mirror-like finish appears. Greater pressure is needed on the pad as the coating builds up. Protect with wax when it is dry.

3. For a waterproof finish, use clear lacquer. Brush or spray on ten to twelve coats and when dry return the piece to the lathe. Use a hard pad or piece of heavy rubbing felt with lacquer rubbing compound and polish the surface as it revolves. Take it easy with pressure; the compound is an abrasive. Protect the surface with wax.

☛ SAFETY SENSE

Wood turning is fascinating; don't spoil the fun by being careless.

1. Roll up your sleeves and remove your tie. Imagine the wear and tear on one's chin should the tie get caught!

2. Always make the setup and any adjustments in it before starting the motor. Use the slower speeds until

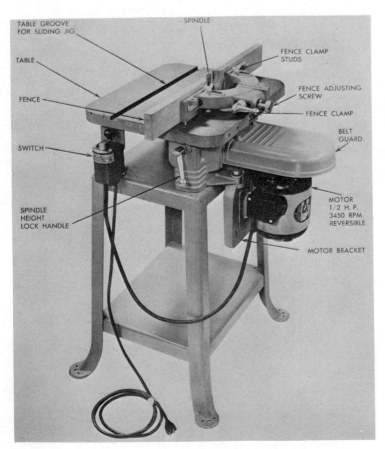

TABLE GROOVE FOR SLIDING JIG

TABLE

FENCE

SWITCH

SPINDLE HEIGHT LOCK HANDLE

SPINDLE

FENCE CLAMP STUDS

FENCE ADJUSTING SCREW

FENCE CLAMP

BELT GUARD

MOTOR 1/2 H. P. 3450 RPM REVERSIBLE

MOTOR BRACKET

Fig. 3—49. The spindle shaper.

Courtesy Rockwell Manufacturing Company

you have had considerable turning experience before you try the faster speeds.

3. Stop the lathe frequently to see that the stock has not worked loose. End play is dangerous in spindle turning. If you hear any strange noises, stop the lathe; the stock may be loose.

4. Try to hold the turning tools so that the chips strike your fingers instead of your face. Use a face shield.

5. If dust bothers you, use a respirator. Remember, dull tools make the most dust.

6. Always remove the tool rest before sanding.

7. When you leave the machine, turn off the motor.

8. Always use finishing cloths folded into pads; they have no ends to get caught.

9. Always turn off the motor and wait until it stops before changing any setup.

THE SPINDLE SHAPER

The work of the spindle shaper is specialized—cutting shaped edges, moldings, picture frame stock, and the like. It takes cutters of varying shapes and whirls them at speeds from 8,000 to 10,000 rpm making smooth, clean cuts.

The Shaper Setup. A typical setup on the shaper employs both halves of the fence, aligned as one. Align them with a straight edge. The desired cutter is placed on the spindle, along with several collars to take up the extra space. The assembly is tightened securely and the table is adjusted for the proper height. Then the fence is moved forward or back to the desired depth of the cut. The motor is started and a piece of scrap stock is run through to test the setup.

Courtesy Rockwell Manufacturing Company

Fig. 3—50. The shaper setup for a cut.

Operating the Shaper. When the setup has been made, every safety precaution must be taken in the operation. The hold-down springs should be used whenever possible. The work is fed from the right side and held firmly against the table and the fence. Enough pressure must be applied to overcome the resistance to the cutting. End grain should be shaped more slowly than the edge to get a smooth cut. The cutters are placed so that the flat sides enter the wood. For some cuts they may be inverted and the motor direction reversed so that the shaping can be done from the bottom side. The work is then fed from the left. This procedure offers an advantage in safety and makes a truer cut in the event that the stock varies in thickness. Always keep the stock moving through the cutters to prevent the wood from burning.

Shaping Irregular Work. The shaper accommodates curves and irregular shapes in addition to straight ones. Because the fence cannot be used for curves, a collar is placed on the spindle to limit the depth of the cut. The edge of the work is guided against this. Necessarily, the edge of the stock must be smooth if the shaping is to be smooth.

This type of shaping is somewhat hazardous, and the work should be fed slowly.

☞ SAFETY SENSE

Shaper safety cannot be overemphasized. The shaper is a machine to be used only by the serious-minded, advanced student. By the time he has acquired competency and control of the machines

Fig. 3—51. The mortiser.

Courtesy Powermatic Machine Company

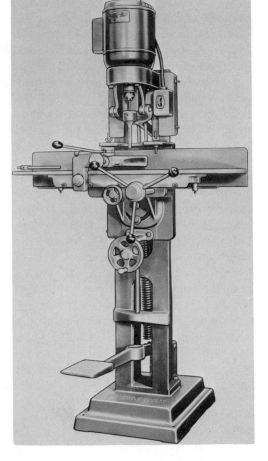

already described, he should be able to use the shaper safely. Consider these suggestions:

1. Never attempt to process a piece of stock which is too small to be held securely in the hands and yet keep the hands well clear of the cutters. So long as the shaper is cutting, the work must be held securely, or else it will be kicked back.

2. The shaper is noisy and this may be distracting to the operator at first. Attention must be focused on the work at all times.

3. Any excessive noise or vibration is a signal to shut off the machine and call the instructor.

THE MORTISER

The mortiser is a single-purpose machine, for the making of mortises only. It operates similar to the attachment for the drill press (see p. 56), except that the chisel is pressed into the wood by a foot lever. Once the setup is made, the operation becomes mechanical.

SANDING MACHINES

There are many types of power sanders: disc, belt, drum, spindle, and sheet. All use abrasive paper or cloth and set it into motion in such a manner as to make light work of sanding. Stationary sanding machines use discs, belts, sheets, and sleeves; portable sanders use discs, belts, or sheets. Sanding follows planing, and when done with successively finer abrasives, it prepares the wood for the finish.

The Disc Sander. This is a motor-driven flat disc to which abrasive paper is cemented. The work is laid on the table and moved back and forth across

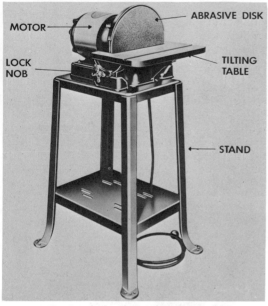

MOTOR

LOCK
NOB

ABRASIVE DISK

TILTING
TABLE

STAND

Courtesy Rockwell Manufacturing Company

Fig. 3—52. The disc sander.

It is difficult to sand an end square or a face flat on the disc sander. The outside of the disc cuts faster than the inside because it travels faster. No adjustments are necessary on this sander except when the table is tilted for beveling.

The abrasive disc is held on by a special adhesive. To replace the disc, remove the old one and turn on the motor. Hold the adhesive stick against the spinning plate. Heat of friction melts the compound. Coat the plate thinly and uniformly. Shut off the motor and place the new disc on the plate. Press it firmly into the adhesive and it is ready to use.

The Belt Sander. The belt sander is simply an endless abrasive belt moving over a pair of drums. It is used on ends, edges, and surfaces. Inside curves can be smoothed on the drums and outside curves on the flat belt.

the revolving disc from the edge to the center, and back. Work on the side of the disc that turns into the table. On the other side, the disc lifts the work away from the table. Work held in the hand may be manipulated against the abrasive.

Light pressure is applied to the back of the belt by the pressure plate held in the hand as in Fig. 3-55. Paste polishing wax is used as the lubricant between the belt and the plate. The abrasive must be kept moving over the work to prevent hollows.

Fig. 3—53 (left). Sanding a miter. Fig. 3—54 (right). Sanding a bevel.

Both photos courtesy Rockwell Manufacturing Company

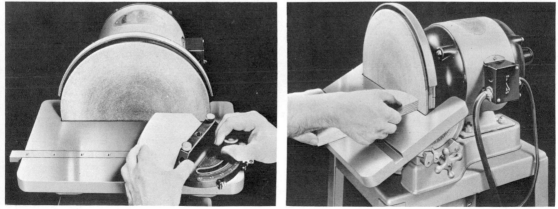

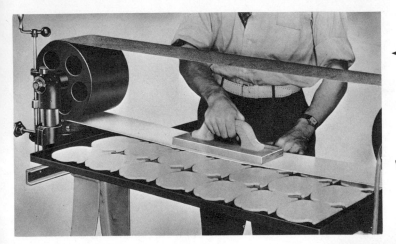

◀ Fig. 3—55. Sanding on the belt sander.

Courtesy Boice-Crane Company

▼ Fig. 3—56. The spindle sander.

Courtesy Boice-Crane Company

When a new belt is installed, two adjustments are necessary. One provides adequate belt tension to keep it from slipping under a load, and the other centers the belt on the drums to keep it in place.

The Drum Sander. The drum sander is a horizontally revolving cylinder, usually about 12″ in diameter, over which the abrasive material is clamped. Both inside and outside curves as well as surfaces may be smoothed on this machine.

The Spindle Sander. The spindle sander is a small version of the drum sander. It is set vertically, and the spindle moves up and down as it revolves. This is the oscillating spindle sander, which is especially suitable for smoothing curved edges. Sanding spindles or drums are also used on the drill press and wood lathe.

☞ SAFETY SENSE

1. Sanding one's fingers produces a painful, slow-healing injury. The moral is to keep the fingers away from the abrasive; the solution is to use the stationary sanding machines only for pieces that can be securely held, with the fingers in the clear.

2. On the floor-type disc sander, sand only on the side which turns into the table.

3. Never turn on a portable sander when it is standing on the abrasive. Pick it up, or lay it over before turning on the motor.

4. Make sure the electric cord is kept clear of the portable sander. It can really get tangled in a belt sander, and when it is cut through, you can imagine what happens!

5. Use little downward pressure on the portable sander. If it does not cut, replace the abrasive. This is less expensive than repairing the machine.

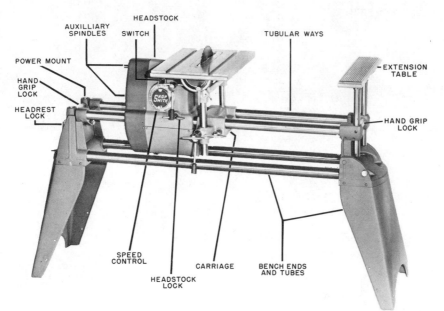

HEADSTOCK

AUXILLIARY
SPINDLES   SWITCH   TUBULAR WAYS

POWER MOUNT
                                                                          EXTENSION
HAND   TABLE
GRIP
LOCK

HEADREST
LOCK   HAND GRIP
                                                                          LOCK

SPEED
CONTROL   CARRIAGE   BENCH ENDS
                                      AND TUBES
HEADSTOCK
LOCK

Courtesy Magna Power Tool Corporation

▲ Fig. 3—57. A multi-purpose machine.

THE MULTI-PURPOSE MACHINE

▼ Fig. 3—58. Raised vertically, the multi-purpose machine becomes a drill press.

The multi-purpose woodworking machine includes as one unit, several machines driven by one motor. The table saw and jointer are a common combination. Others include the table saw, jointer, wood lathe, drill press, sander, and even more. This machine has particular advantage for the home workshop. It is more economical of space than the same number of individual machines, and its cost is less. Engineering-wise, some of these combinations are marvels of ingenuity. The problem of changing from one process to another has been simplified so that a minimum of assembling and disassembling is required.

Operation of the individual machine tools is essentially the same as that of unit machines. When the multi-purpose machine is so designed that only one

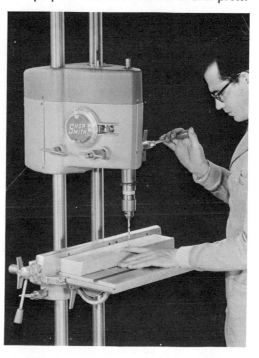

Courtesy Magna Power Tool Corporation

Fig. 3—59. Spindle turning on the lathe. The multi-purpose machine is set up to cut a taper.

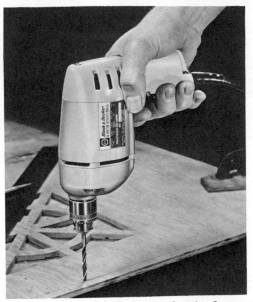

Courtesy Black and Decker Manufacturing Company

Fig. 3—60 (above). A ¼" portable electric drill. In actual operation, two hands are recommended. Fig. 3—61 (below). Driving wood screws with a portable electric drill. A speed reducing unit replaces the chuck.

process can be performed at one time, a potential safety hazard is eliminated.

PORTABLE MACHINE TOOLS

In recent years, portable machine tools have become so common as to replace many hand tools. The number and variety continue to increase. These tools are for the most part easier and faster to use than the hand tools they replace. Most of them are two-handed tools. Be sure to remember this. Two hands increase your control of the tool and make for safest operation. These tools should always be grounded when in use, unless, of course, they are battery-operated. They are available with a ground wire in the cord and a three-pronged plug for a grounded receptacle.

THE ELECTRIC DRILL

The portable electric drill is one of the most versatile of power tools. It is

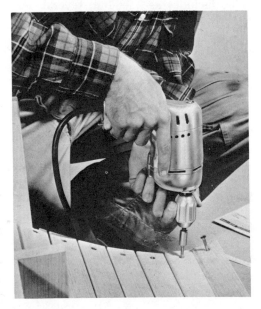

actually a portable power unit which not only can drill holes but can accommodate a number of attachments. These include disc and belt sanders, screwdrivers, saber and circular saws, buffers, polishers, and others. Battery operated drills are available. Besides being most portable, there is no chance of electric shock with them.

Electric drills come in different capacities based on the maximum diameter of the straight shank drill bit they accept: ¼″, ⅜″, or ½″. The bit is locked with a chuck key. Although the drill usually has a pistol grip, use two hands to support and control it. To start a hole at an exact point, press the bit into the wood before turning on the motor. Then press only hard enough to keep the bit cutting. Ease up on the pressure as the bit cuts through the opposite side. To clear out the chips, keep the bit turning as you withdraw it from the hole.

Fig. 3—62. A saber saw is an all-purpose tool. The blade cuts on the up stroke.

Courtesy Stanley Tools

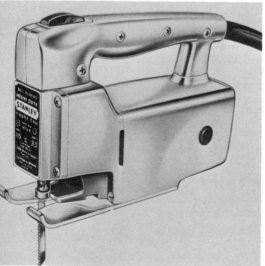

Courtesy Black and Decker Manufacturing Company

Fig. 3—63. A saber saw making a bevel cut. The saw tilts on the guide.

THE SABER SAW

The saber saw is one of the handiest of the light machine tools. A portable jig saw, this tool crosscuts, rips, and cuts scrolls in wood, wall board, and plastics. It also is a power hack saw for metals. In use, the saw must be carefully guided by hand. It should be pushed ahead only as fast as it can cut. Too much push will break the blade. A plunge cut can be made through a board so that boring a starting hole is not necessary. Tilt the saw until it rests on the base plate and the tip of the blade. Turn on the motor and press down gently on the blade. There are special blades for different materials.

ELECTRIC HAND SAW

This saw is a portable circular saw especially useful for crosscutting, ripping, and mitering. It can be used with an attached guide or it can be moved along a straight board clamped to the work, as a fence. Like all circular saws, it cuts very fast. When the switch is in the handle, be careful not to squeeze it accidentally. The saw should be running before the blade contacts the wood and should be shut off as soon as the blade clears the cut. A face shield is recommended since this saw tends to throw sawdust.

Sizes are given as the diameter of the blade and are commonly 5″, 6″, 7″, and 8″, with proportionally powerful motors and increasing weight. Since this saw is a self-contained unit, all adjustments are made on the machine. Depth of cut, width, angle, and bevel are all provided for. The built-in guard functions in all positions and for all cuts.

Fig. 3—64. The electric hand saw is a portable circular saw. It is available in different sizes. The larger, the more muscle required to control it.

Courtesy Black and Decker Manufacturing Company

 SAFETY SENSE

1. This saw requires the use of both hands for accurate control of the cut, and when operated in this manner, permits little chance for injury.
2. The stock should be held securely, preferably clamped in a vise, to prevent movement during cutting.
3. The motor should be turned on before the blade strikes the work.
4. As in all portable electric machines there is a tendency to overlook the ground connection. This connection is particularly important on machines used out of doors. One should not need to be shocked to realize it.

ALL-PURPOSE ELECTRIC SAW

This tool is literally a power hand saw. It cuts on the pull stroke and, with the proper blades, can be used on wood or metal. Apply only enough downward pressure on the blade to keep it cutting. Riding it will break the blade.

Fig. 3—65. The all-purpose saw is relatively new to the field. It operates similar to the saber saw except that the blade is horizontal.

Courtesy Stanley Tools

THE ELECTRIC PLANE

The portable electric plane has a motor-driven cutter set in a frame which is held and pushed as a hand plane. The depth of cut is adjustable. The tool must be held firmly in contact with the wood. It will cut as true an edge as a jointer of the same size. You may note that it resembles a jointer upside down.

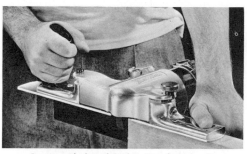

Courtesy Black and Decker Manufacturing Company

Fig. 3—66. The electric plane is a portable jointer.

THE ROUTER-SHAPER

The router is a portable shaper that is moved over the work instead of the work being moved through the cutter, as in the regular shaper. The router is light enough to be held in the hands and to be guided free-hand over a surface for carving and routing out backgrounds. It may be mounted upside down in a fixture and used as a shaper. This is why it is often called a router-shaper. A great assortment of cutters is available. This machine, like the shaper, turns at a high speed. The cutter must be locked on securely. With a special jig, dovetail joints are easily and accurately made.

The depth of cut is adjusted by screwing the guide up or down the body

Courtesy Porter-Cable Machine Company

Fig. 3—67. Shaping irregular work with a router-shaper.

of the machine. Collars are used as on the shaper, to determine the width of the cut and to permit it to follow curves. Some cutters have integral collars or guides.

The router is a very flexible machine. It will follow irregular curves or straight lines. It is safer to use than the shaper if for no other reason than that both hands

Fig. 3—68. Cutting an edge mold with a router-shaper.

Courtesy Porter-Cable Machine Company

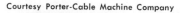

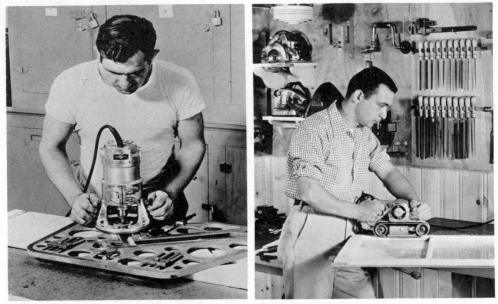

Both photographs courtesy Porter-Cable Machine Company

Fig. 3—69 (left). Routing out a pattern.
Fig. 3—70 (right). Using the portable belt sander in the home workshop.

are required to hold the handles, thus preventing the fingers from getting into the cutter. With router bits the machine cuts in all directions; with shaper cutters, in one direction only.

The torque of the motor must be overcome by holding the machine securely. The motor should not be turned on unless the router is being held, either by hand or in a jig. When it is being used as a shaper, the safety precautions for that machine apply.

PORTABLE SANDERS

Portable sanders include the heavy duty floor sanders as well as the light, hand type. The latter are of concern here.

The Portable Belt Sander. This is the heaviest of the portable sanders and requires the most strength to control. As the belt turns on the drums, it tends to pull the machine away from the operator. Enough resistance to control this tendency must be supplied in order to use it. Beginners often "ride" this machine by applying downward pressure. This causes uneven cutting, a slipping belt, and even a burned-out motor. The weight of the machine provides the pressure necessary on the belt; it only is necessary to maneuver the machine uniformly over the surface. Should it remain a little too long in the same spot, it cuts a hollow. It should be used only in the direction of the grain.

Lay the machine on its side when not in use. Never turn on the motor while it is standing on the belt. It may run off the bench.

The Portable Disc Sander. This is a vertical motor with a flexible rubber disc supporting the abrasive. It too, must be kept in motion to prevent cutting hollows. It is most useful for rough sanding, since it always cuts across the grain (see Fig. 3-52).

Oscillating Sanders. The oscillating and orbital sanders are light in weight and easy to control. They use a flat sheet of abrasive, moving it in short, rapid strokes. The oscillating sander moves the abrasive back and forth in a straight line. This is preferred for the finest finish. The orbital sander moves the abrasive in an orbit, or circle. Care must be used here to prevent scratching the surface as the abrasive cuts across the grain.

Courtesy Porter-Cable Machine Company

Fig. 3—71. Finish sanding with a portable oscillating sander.

🖝 **SAFETY SENSE**

1. Unplug any portable electric tool when making an adjustment, such as changing the depth of cut, the blade, installing a bit, sander belt, and the like.

2. Always ground a portable electric tool when in use. Watch where you stand, too, when operating it. Damp floors can be dangerous.

3. Do not overload a power tool or use it for jobs which are beyond its capacity.

4. Look for the Underwriters' Laboratory seal of approval on a power tool when you buy. This is your assurance that it meets the electrical standards set by that agency. The seal should be on the tool, not just on the cord.

FOR RESEARCH, EXPERIMENT, DEVELOPMENT

1. How is the rotary motion of the motor changed to a vertical reciprocating motion in the jig saw?
2. Why is the splitter on a circular saw guard a necessary safety feature?
3. Why does a band saw cut faster than a jig saw?
4. How can you make sure that your circular saw will make a square cut?
5. Which cuts can be made best on the circular saw, and which on the radial saw?
6. How are injuries most likely to occur on the circular saw?
7. How does one know when the blade is dull and should be replaced?
8. Why is a jointer with dull blades noisier than one with sharp blades?
9. When is it better to rabbet on a jointer than on a circular saw?
10. Why is the saw blade usually held on with a left-hand nut?

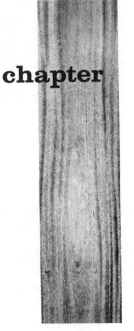

chapter 4

WOOD
STRUCTURES

What is the best way to fasten two pieces of wood together? This is the key question that the woodworker must answer in any and all of the projects he makes. Joints are usually the weakest parts in wood construction. Most of the skill and know-how in woodwork centers about the making of good joints and structures, many of which are the same as those used hundreds of years ago. They were logical answers to the above question then, and are still preferred.

As machines took over the production of wood products in industry, wood joinery became quite standardized. For example, the blind mortise and tenon joint was nearly always used with table legs and rails. This joint can be made quickly and accurately by machine and is a good answer to the key question. Since the professional designer has taken over much of the product design in this

country, different ideas of joinery and structures have appeared, as well as those of function and form. The designer in his search for new, different, better, and more economical ideas for products has given as much attention to the problem of fastening materials together as to the selection of materials. Consequently, table construction, and this is only one example, is different today. This is especially noticeable in coffee and occasional tables.

JOINTS AS STRUCTURES

The cabinet maker of by-gone days was a master at his craft when he could fit his joints together so well that they were difficult to find. Professional furniture designers today see no particular advantage in making joinery invisible. They often prefer to use joinery that shows how the pieces fit together. This promotes a feeling of genuineness and straight forwardness and adds to the aesthetic quality as well.

In the details of the structures that follow, the common, most logical joints are shown. You can use these as they are, or you can work out combinations. Perhaps you can effectively combine metals with wood. No matter what joints you use, they are strong only when they fit well. Instructions here are for hand-made joints. When using machines, the fundamental cuts are employed; for example: squaring, mitering, rabbeting, dadoing, and the like.

Butt Joints:

Types: end butt; edge butt.

Nature: simple and quick, they are used more in carpentry than in furniture. Gluing tends to be less effective on end grain. Nails, screws, various types of metal fasteners, and dowels (see **Fig. 4-1**) may be used.

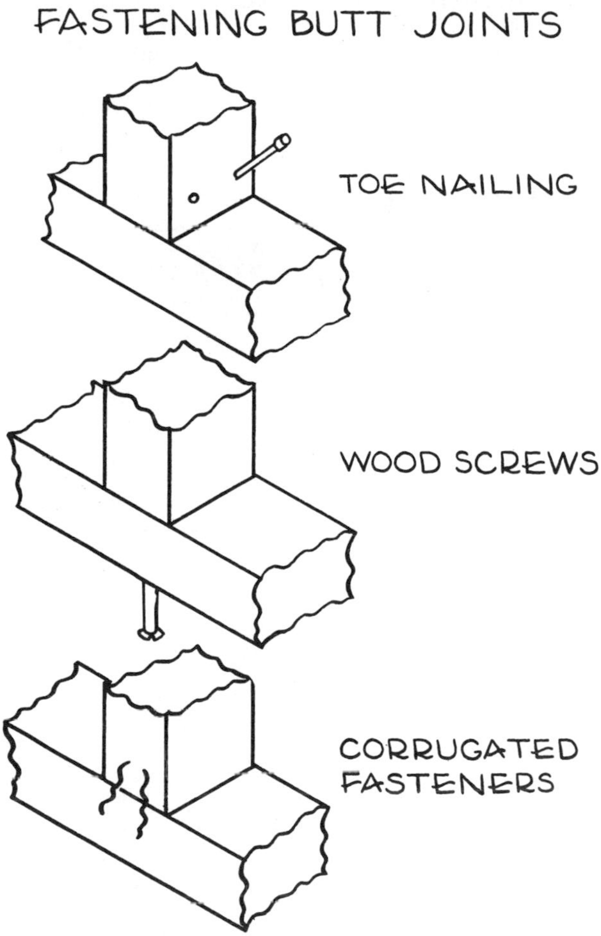

FASTENING BUTT JOINTS

TOE NAILING

WOOD SCREWS

CORRUGATED FASTENERS

Fig. 4—1. Fastening butt joints.

Dado Joints:

Types: dado and butt; dado and rabbet. The dado is the cut, or groove, across the grain.

Nature: the dado helps in assembly. Glue is effective. Nails and screws are also used. The depth of the dado should be from ⅓ to ½ the thickness of the stock.

Lap Joints:

Types: half lap; cross lap; end lap; middle lap; scarf.

Nature: when the joints are flush, as shown in Fig. 4-3, the lap is cut halfway through each piece. Glue alone is adequate for fastening, assuming that the parts fit well.

Construction (for both lap and dado joints):

1. Mark out the joint accurately, using a knife and try-square.
2. Hold the piece in a vise; clamp on a guide block for the back saw.
3. Make the end cuts first.
4. Using as wide a wood chisel as possible, clean out the waste.
5. For a machined joint, use the dado head on a circular saw.

Rabbet Joints:

Types: end rabbet and butt; edge rabbet and butt.

Nature: these provide simple but ef-

DADO JOINTS

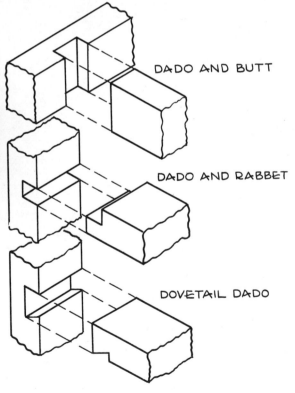

DADO AND BUTT

DADO AND RABBET

DOVETAIL DADO

Fig. 4–2. Dado joints.
Fig. 4–3. Lap joints.

LAP JOINTS

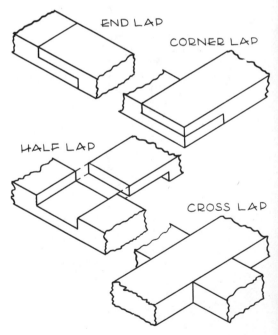

END LAP

CORNER LAP

HALF LAP

CROSS LAP

RABBET JOINTS

RABBET AND BUTT

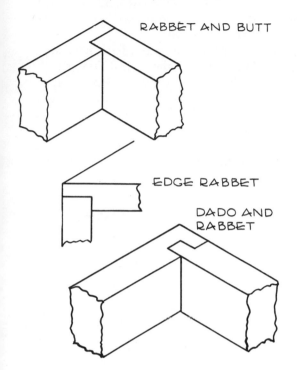

EDGE RABBET

DADO AND
RABBET

Fig. 4—4. Rabbet joints.

MITER JOINTS

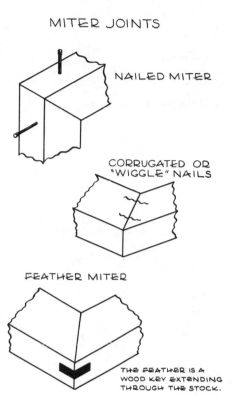

NAILED MITER

CORRUGATED OR
"WIGGLE" NAILS

FEATHER MITER

THE FEATHER IS A
WOOD KEY EXTENDING
THROUGH THE STOCK.

Fig. 4—5. Miter joints.

fective corner construction. Glue holds the edge joint. Screws may be used.
Construction: the rabbet and butt can be made by hand. The edge rabbet and butt is best made on a jointer or circular saw.

Miter Joints:
Types: butt; splined or feathered.
Nature: miter joints are those whose parts are cut at angles other than 90 and 180 degrees. The spline is cut on the circular saw. It is assembled with adhesive and is the strongest of the three.
Construction: use a miter box when making this joint by hand. For assembly, use a miter vise preferably. With a bench vise, clamp the parts in the proper posi-

tion and drive a nail from each side, with alternate hammer blows to keep the parts from sliding (see Fig. 7-3).

Dowel Joints:
Types: edge; corner.
Nature: the dowels keep the parts in alignment but do not hold them together. Dowels are helpful when gluing long stock edge to edge, as in table tops. Use at least three in this type of jointing.
Construction:
1. Use a doweling jig whenever possible (see Fig. 4-6).
2. Mark both edges of the pieces at **the** same time to assure accurate location of the holes.
3. Set the jig over the mark and bore

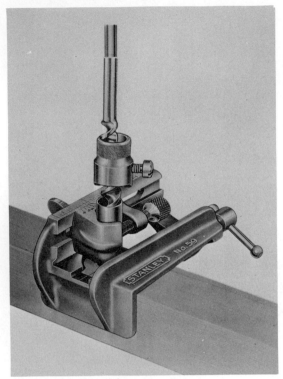

Courtesy Stanley Tools

Fig. 4—6. A doweling jig.

Construction:

1. To make the joint by hand, mark out the two parts accurately with a knife and a try square.
2. Cut the tenon with a back saw, staying outside of the marks. True it with a chisel.
3. Bore out the mortise on the drill press, although a brace and bit can be used also.
4. Remove the waste, square up the mortise with a chisel, and fit the two parts snugly.

DOWEL JOINTS

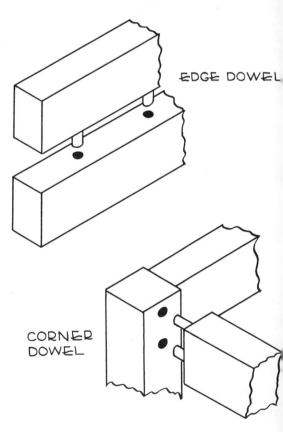

Fig. 4—7 Dowel joints.

the hole with brace and bit, using a bit stop. Make the holes the same size as the dowels. Spiral-cut pegs hold more firmly than plain-cut.

Mortise and Tenon Joints:

Types: blind; through.

Nature: there are many variations of these two types. They require precise workmanship if they are to be worthwhile. The mortise is the socket; the tenon fits into it. Construction of the tenon on the circular saw is facilitated with a tenoning jig. The mortiser, drill press, or router is used in making the mortise.

Locked Joints. Mortise and tenon joints can be locked securely and permanently with pegs and wedges. Dowels can be glued through the assembly. The end of a through tenon can be split gently with a wood chisel and a slender wooden wedge driven in. Glue should be applied to the wedge. The mortise can be tapered slightly so that the open end is wider. The wedge will now make the joint permanent.

Leg tenons coming through a table top can be locked with a wedge to provide added interest to the construction. The end grain of the tenon should run parallel or opposite to the grain in the top. The wedge may be of a contrasting color and should be inserted parallel to the grain of the tenon.

Fig. 4—9. Boring out the mortise on the drill press.

MORTISE AND TENON JOINTS

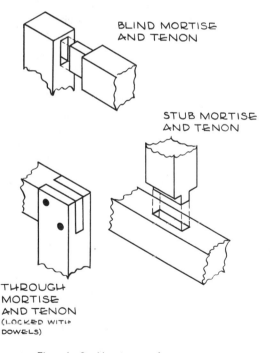

BLIND MORTISE
AND TENON

STUB MORTISE
AND TENON

THROUGH
MORTISE
AND TENON
(LOCKED WITH
DOWELS)

Fig. 4—8. Mortise and tenon joints.

JOINTS LOCKED WITH WEDGES

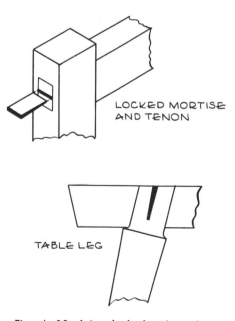

LOCKED MORTISE
AND TENON

TABLE LEG

Fig. 4—10. Joints locked with wedges.

DOVETAIL JOINTS

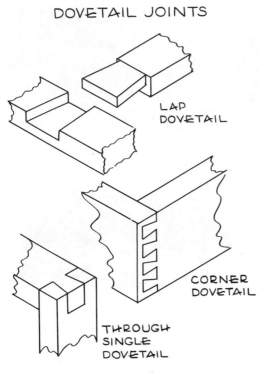

Fig. 4—11. Dovetail joints.

Courtesy Porter-Cable Machine Company

Fig. 4—12. Cutting dovetails with a router and a jig.

Dovetail Joints:

Common types: lap; through; half-blind; dado.

Nature: the dovetail joint is so-named because of its wedge-shaped pin, which resembles the tail of a dove. It is self-locking and commonly used in drawer construction in better furniture. This joint is best made on a router with a dovetail cutter.

EDGE JOINTS

Types: butt; tongue and groove; spline; ship lap.

Nature: to make a wide board from several narrow ones requires edge jointing. Several methods are used (see Fig. 4-13).

Edge Butt Joint. A plain, glued butt joint is adequate when the stock is true and the pieces are short enough to be easily clamped, say up to 24″. Completely true contact between the two edges gives the maximum strength with gluing. With the edges in place, no light should be visible between them, nor should they rock. On longer pieces, test the fit by inserting a slender strip of newspaper between the edges and sliding it along. When it cannot slide at any point, contact is excellent. When it slides, then stops, it has struck a high point which must be removed. Long boards are difficult to clamp when gluing because they shift.

Dowel Joint. Dowel pegs in the butt joint make it easy to hold the position while clamping. Three pegs are usually enough when the stock is true. If the boards are slightly curved, add a few more. Pegs need to be only about two inches long, entering each board one inch. For 1″ stock, use ⅜″ diameter dowel. Your teacher may have some ready-cut pegs with spiral grooves for better gluing. Be sure the holes are deep enough.

Tongue and Groove Joint. The tongue and groove joint can be cut on a shaper, or on the circular saw. This is an easy joint to assemble. Make the width of the tongue no more than one-half the thickness of the board.

Spline Joint. The spline joint involves the use of a slender strip, or spline, inserted into matching grooves in the edges of the boards. The grooves can be cut on the circular saw. For 1″ stock make the spline up to ½″ thick.

Ship Lap Joint. The ship lap joint gets its name from the fact that it was originally used in ship construction, especially in the planking. It is a double rabbet or an edge lap joint, but it is difficult to clamp.

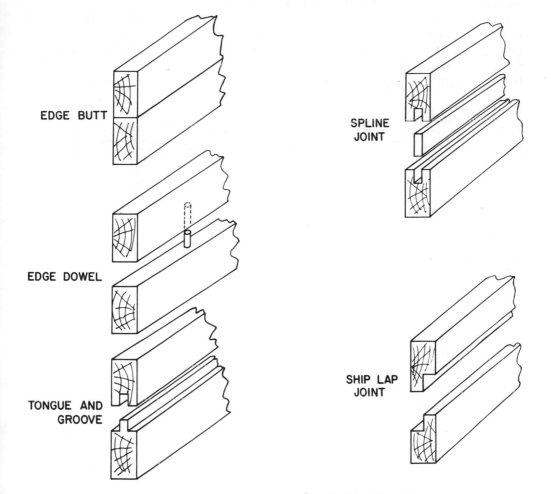

EDGE BUTT

EDGE DOWEL

TONGUE AND GROOVE

SPLINE JOINT

SHIP LAP JOINT

Fig. 4—13. Edge joints.

BENDING WOOD

Curves are formed in wood by cutting or by bending. For some curves, cutting may be extremely wasteful and, for others, bending may be impossible. The woodworker must know which method is the better for the job at hand.

Bending is done with solid stock, with laminations, and with plywoods. When plasticizing is needed, steaming or soaking are the most common treatments. Chemical treatments have been devised for softening wood, but they have not as yet replaced the water method.

Wood for Bending. All woods do not bend equally well, nor do all pieces from the same board. Hardwoods are preferred to softwoods when a sharp bending is required. The stock should be straight-grained, free from knots, and uniform in density for best results. According to the United States Department of Agriculture *Wood Handbook*, soaking and steaming makes it possible to compress some woods as much as 25 to 30 per cent on the inside of the bend, although the outside may stretch only 1 to 2 per cent. This limitation may or may not be objectionable. Curves in metal, plastic, and clay products are often excessive. Because only simple, graceful curves are possible in bent wood, they are less likely to be carried to excess.

Bent wood is affected by changes in moisture content. Absorption tends to flatten the curve, while drying tends to increase it. A thorough sealing of the wood with a finish helps to control the shape.

Steaming and Soaking. Steaming and soaking in boiling water can be done in any convenient container. An ordinary home laundry wash boiler is useful for larger pieces. For steaming, the stock can be laid on a rack just above the water. Small pieces can be immersed in a wire basket like french fries.

Whether to steam or to soak the wood is determined by trial. Small thin stock can be adequately softened by steam, but thick stock may need a soaking. The latter is generally quicker. The time required for the treatment is also found by experiment. The larger and the denser the stock, the longer the time for processing. Excessive soaking causes the color of some woods to fade.

Bending. The amount of bending possible depends not only on the wood itself, but also on the plasticizing treatment, and on the construction of the bending jig. When two or more pieces are to be

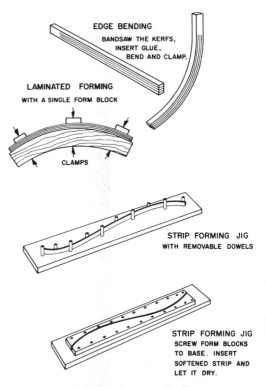

EDGE BENDING
BANDSAW THE KERFS,
INSERT GLUE,
BEND AND CLAMP.

LAMINATED FORMING
WITH A SINGLE FORM BLOCK

CLAMPS

STRIP FORMING JIG
WITH REMOVABLE DOWELS

STRIP FORMING JIG
SCREW FORM BLOCKS
TO BASE. INSERT
SOFTENED STRIP AND
LET IT DRY.

Fig. 4—14. Bending methods.

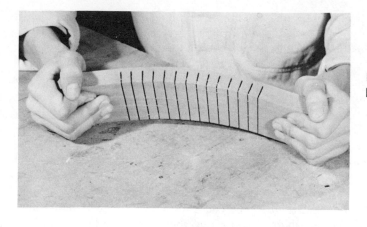

Fig. 4—15. Bending wood by cutting across the grain.

bent similarly, a jig is necessary for holding the stock until it is dry. The jig should be designed for ease of loading, so that the stock can be quickly locked in place while moist and hot. Some allowance for spring-back is necessary, perhaps as much as 5 to 10 per cent, especially in heavy stock. When the stock is as heavy as an inch in thickness, the jig must be very strongly built; the wood, even after steaming, still resists bending.

Bending with Laminations. Laminations are thin sections of wood which are bonded together with adhesive. Laminating is used to get the sharpest bends and the greatest strength from the least wood. Curves may be formed during the laminating process, or after it is complete, and with or without steaming. The direction of the grain in the laminations may be alternated, as in plywood. When the part to be formed is long and slender, as in skis and table legs, the grain should run the long way.

The thinner the stock, the sharper the bend that is possible. Veneer stock may be bent to as little as a 2″ radius, and even smaller when steamed. Thin laminations add up to greater strength than do thick ones, because of the strength of the adhesive.

The jig for holding the laminations in place must also permit the application of pressure uniformly over the stock during the setting of the adhesive. Blocks may be cut to fit the inside and outside of the curves and the laminations clamped between them. When possible, apply the adhesive to all of the pieces at once, lay them quickly in order, and insert the assembly into the jig.

Bending Plywood. Thin plywood bends easily in either direction. A strip of 1/16″ three-ply birch, for example, can actually be tied in a knot. Such stock can be used for laminating. It is especially adapted to model construction. Steaming and soaking is limited to plywood bonded with waterproof adhesives.

Bending Wood by Cutting. Cutting saw kerfs in wood relieves the stiffness, making bends possible. However, strength is decreased with each cut. To bend wood in the direction of the grain, the kerfs must be made across the grain. The deeper the cuts and the closer together, the sharper the wood bends. Steaming may be desirable in addition to the cutting, although it is usually unnecessary.

Saw kerfs on the underside of a solid wood table help to minimize warping a stiff board. These cuts should run in the direction of the grain, an inch or two apart, and as deep as one-half to three-fourths of the thickness. Extend them as near the ends as possible. Such cutting makes the piece somewhat flexible. Fill the kerfs with glue.

Veneering. The bonding of surface veneers to core stock can be done easily in the home workshop or in the school shop, provided adequate clamping equipment is available. Special veneer presses are available, although for small jobs ordinary C clamps and wood screw clamps will do. The adhesive is best applied with a roller to both surfaces. With the veneer in place it should be rolled with a heavy brayer, or even a rolling pin, from the center out to the edges to remove any trapped air. A smooth pressure block large enough to cover the veneer is then clamped in place. Center clamps should be applied first.

WHICH STRUCTURES SHOULD YOU USE?

This question always faces the woodworker. There is no simple answer. Our suggestion is that you use as simple a structure as will provide the strength and durability desired. With machines you can produce joints which fit more accurately than those made by hand, so machine-made joints can be more complex. Those in furniture require the greatest of accuracy. A wood product or project is no better than its joints. Study the structures in the Project Ideas section. You will see some simple, unusual, but effective types. Perhaps you can design your own joints. It may be well for you to make a model of the joint in scrap material to see what it will look like and to find the best way to construct it.

FOR RESEARCH, EXPERIMENT, DEVELOPMENT

1. Why must a glue joint fit perfectly?
2. Why may a poorly-fitting mortise and tenon joint be less durable than a well-fitting simpler joint?
3. Why does a piece of wood bend less easily than a piece of mild steel?
4. How does one make the best selection of joints to use in a project?
5. Why does laminating make especially strong construction?
6. Test the comparative strengths of different kinds of woods. Suspend weights from the center of supported strips of the same cross-sectional area.
7. In a hydraulic press, run comparison compression tests of end grain, edge grain, and face grain wood.
8. Compare the bend strengths of solid and laminated wood.

chapter 5

ABRASIVES

Abrasives serve the same purpose for all materials: cutting, shaping, and smoothing. They are rarely used for cutting in woodwork, because sawing is much faster. Soft woods such as balsa can be shaped quickly and often completely on a sander. In the smoothing process, tool marks are removed with coarse abrasives that leave scratches. These in turn are removed by increasingly finer grades.

Abrasives for wood are usually crushed rock; either flint or garnet. Steel wool is sometimes used on curved surfaces. Powdered pumice stone, rotten stone (limestone), and prepared rubbing compounds are used for smoothing and polishing finished surfaces. Abrasive coated paper is called sandpaper, even though sand is not used. Grains of sand have rounded edges and would be useless for cutting. Particles of tungsten carbide brazed to thin metal sheet are used as the abrasive for power sanders.

Aluminum oxide coated abrasives can be used for either hand or power sanding.

SANDPAPER

Kinds and Grades of Sandpaper. Sandpaper for wood is usually flint paper and garnet paper. The particles are bonded to the paper with glue, their sharp edges erect. This is done by an electrocoating process in which the grains are attracted to the glue surface or by a gravity process in which the particles are sifted onto the sticky glue. The degree of coarseness of the abrasive is given either by number, symbol, or class. For example, a No. 50 grit, a 1-0, and medium all specify essentially the same abrasive coarseness of particles.

Sheet sizes are usually 9″ x 11″. Flint paper costs less than garnet, but garnet outwears flint and may be more economical in the long run. Water-proof abrasive paper is used for rubbing and polishing finishes with water.

The use of abrasive cloth is becoming increasingly common as sanding machines do more and more of the sanding. Instead of paper backing, cloth is used to make the abrasive most durable. Garnet and aluminum oxide grains are the common types of abrasive cloth. Aluminum oxide is graded by number.

How to Use Sandpaper: Although sanding machines lessen the labor, hand sanding is still necessary. Coarser grades cut faster; for the first sanding, therefore, one should use as coarse a grade as is appropriate to the job. If however, the work is so rough that medium garnet paper is too fine, perhaps it would be better to do the preliminary smoothing by planing or filing. When roughing out a block of balsa to shape, grades ½″ or even 1 may be the best choice, but they might scratch walnut or mahogany so deeply that it would take extra work to remove the cuts.

Suggestions for Sanding:

1. Use a grade of paper coarse enough to remove the tool marks but not so coarse that it will replace them with deeper cuts.

2. On the flat grain and edge grain, always sand in the direction of the grain. Try sanding across grain on a piece of scrap; notice the deep scratches. It takes a lot of sanding to get rid of them. Even when one thinks they have been removed, they appear boldly through the finish. When sanding the edge grain, try to follow the direction of the annual rings.

3. When the tool marks have been removed with the coarse paper, use successively finer grades, for example, 1-0, 3-0, and 6-0, depending on how smooth the surface should be.

4. To keep edges straight and faces flat, use sandpaper on a block. A block of wood of convenient size will do. It is most economical to cut the paper

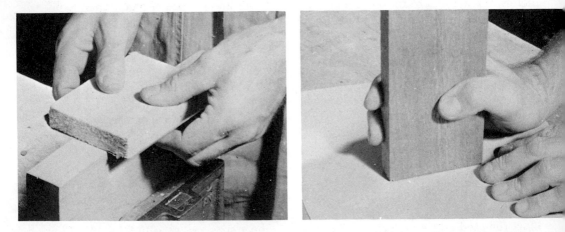

Fig. 5—1 (above, left). Sanding an edge with a block. Note how the fingers serve as a guide to keep the edge square with the faces. Fig. 5—2 (above, right). Sanding an end on a sheet of abrasive.

into quarters, nearly square, and use a block to fit. Incidentally, cutting sandpaper on a regular paper cutter helps to keep the cutter sharp.

5. For sanding rounded surfaces, either concave or convex, use the paper in your hand, or over a flexible felt or rubber pad.

6. To sand short edges and ends true, lay a full sheet of sandpaper on a flat surface and rub the wood over the sandpaper.

7. When sanding curved edges, such as on jigsaw cut-outs, wrap sandpaper around the file you have been using, or around dowel sticks of assorted diameters.

8. For fine details, glue sandpaper on tongue depressors or ice cream bar sticks, using rubber cement. Emery boards usually used for smoothing fingernails are useful, too.

9. When the cutting edges of the abrasive are worn smooth, discard the paper. Much time can be wasted with

Courtesy Yates-American Machine Company

Fig. 5—4. Industrial sanding machine.

worn-out paper. Any piece of wood can be made only so smooth; watch the surface as you sand. If it is not getting smoother, it is time to stop.

STEEL WOOL

This cutting material is especially useful for smoothing curved surfaces, such as in wood turning and on sculptured free forms. It is graded by number and class; for example, 3-0 is fine, and 1-0 is medium. It should be used in as large a pad as can be handled in order to distribute the pressure over a large area.

WATERPROOF PAPER

Waterproof abrasive papers are intended for use in smoothing finishes. After a coat of varnish or enamel has dried, it can be smoothed with a piece of 6-0 or 8-0 paper dipped frequently in water. Water keeps the particles of abrasive from becoming clogged. It serves as lubricant to protect the finish. A smoother surface is possible with water. This is the same type of abrasive

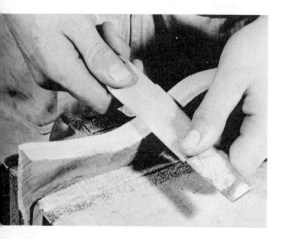

Fig. 5—3. Wrapping abrasive paper around a file makes sanding curves much easier.

as is used in preparing automobile finishes for the final coat. It is not used on the final coat of any finish unless a dull effect is desired.

POLISHING COMPOUNDS

Abrasives are available as powders and as pastes for polishing finishes, usually for the final coat. Pumice stone is used with water. Rotten stone (talc) is used with light mineral oil. The latter is the softest of the natural rock abrasives. Use it on a heavy felt pad. Prepared paste polishing compounds contain fine aluminum oxide, iron oxide (rouge), or other such abrasives. They are used particularly on lacquer and plastic finishes.

A COMPARISON OF SANDPAPER
ABRASIVE GRADES

CLASS	FLINT SYMBOL	GRAIN NO.	GARNET SYMBOL	CLASS	FLINT SYMBOL	GRAIN NO.	GARNET SYMBOL
Very Fine	7–0	320		Medium (Continued)	1		
	6–0	280	8–0			60	½
	5–0	240	7–0		1½	50	1
	4–0	220	6–0				
Fine	3–0	180	5–0				
		150	4–0	Coarse	2	40	1½
	2–0				2½	36	2
		120	3–0			30	2½
	0				3		
Medium	½			Very Coarse	3½	24	3
		80	1–0			20	3½

FOR RESEARCH, EXPERIMENT, DEVELOPMENT

1. What does the cutting on an abrasive?
2. How are sandpaper scratches in a wood surface eliminated?
3. Why are joints in wood not sanded before assembling?
4. How does one tell which are the proper grades of sandpaper for a job?
5. When is steel wool better than sandpaper for smoothing a wood surface?
6. How is sandpaper coated with abrasive?
7. What is the hardest natural stone?
8. Why does sanding across the grain leave scratches?
9. Why does sanding with the grain leave no scratches?
10. Why is it so difficult to sand square an edge or an end by hand?

chapter 6

FASTENERS

In the early days, fastening logs or boards together securely and permanently was difficult and awkward. Tying with rope had its limitations, as did the use of wooden pegs. Later, iron nails simplified the joining, and since their invention a great many other fastening devices have been developed. Common fasteners now include many types of nails, screws, tacks, bolts, and the like. It is important to know which fasteners to use in woodwork. For example, in fine furniture, nails are rarely used. Only an amateur would use nails to fasten such fine woods as walnut and mahogany.

NAILS

The first nails were forged by hand by the village blacksmith. Today they are made from wire in automatic machines. They are installed by driving with a claw hammer, the nail hammer. They can be removed from the joint, but usually not without damage to the wood. When clinched on the back side, they form a permanent joint. Only enough nails should be used to give the desired strength; too many weaken the joint by splitting the wood. Install the nails so that they do not fall into the same line of wood grain. Holding power is much greater in dense woods than in the softer woods. For instance, nails in balsa are useless, they can be pushed in by hand and removed just as easily. Slanting the nails increases holding power.

Kinds of Nails. Many different kinds of nails are available, each designed for a different use. Several metals are employed, including iron, steel, brass, copper, monel, and aluminum. Steel nails may be coated with zinc or plated with copper or brass to prevent rust. They may be coated with cement or rosin to increase their holding. The shape of the head is determined by the intended use.

The kinds of nails most commonly used in woodworking include *common, finish, casing, box,* and *wire brads* and *wire nails.* The first three are for building construction work. The small heads of the finish and casing nails make it pos-

TYPES OF BUILDING NAILS

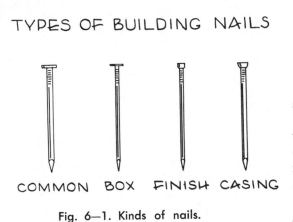

COMMON   BOX   FINISH   CASING

Fig. 6—1. Kinds of nails.

sible to set them below the surface and to fill the hole with wood putty. Box nails are smaller in diameter and are used in box construction. Wire brads and wire nails resemble finish and common nails respectively, but are available in a greater number of sizes.

Special Nails. Corrugated fasteners, sometimes called "wrinkle" or "wiggle" nails provide a quick, temporary joining of soft woods, as in miter joints. They are seldom appropriate in furniture. Double-pointed tacks and upholsterers

tacks are used for similar purposes. The latter are often called carpet tacks and are sized by length or by number with the ⅜" length equivalent to a No. 2½. Upholsterer's nails are the decorative head nails used in upholstery. Escutcheon pins are round head brass nails, sized by length and gauge number.

Sizes of Nails. The sizes of carpenters' nails are given in "d's" as 6d, 8d, and so on. The d is the English symbol for penny and is still used, even though details of the system have been lost. Here are the sizes of common, finish, and casing nails:

2d	1"	16d	3½"
4d	1½"	20d	4"
6d	2"	30d	4½"
8d	2½"	40d	5"
10d	3"	50d	5½"
12d	3½"	60d	6"

Wire Nails and Wire Brads. Common sizes of wire nails and brads range from ¼", No. 20, to 3", No. 10. The larger the wire gauge number, the smaller the nail diameter. A No. 15 brad is approximately ¹⁄₁₆" and is about twice as heavy as a No. 20.

WOOD SCREWS

Wood screws are fastening devices that use screw threads to do the holding. The screw is driven, or screwed, into a hole with a screw driver, and, as it turns, it cuts threads in the wood. A wood screw holds much better than a nail and has the advantage of being easily removed, permitting the dissembly of the project. Screws are machine-made from wire.

Kinds of Wood Screws. Wood screws are available in many styles and sizes to suit many purposes. They are classified according to the kind of head, the ma-

COMMON TYPES OF WOOD SCREWS

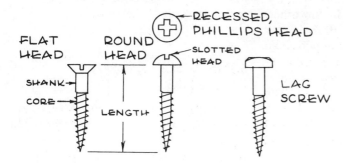

FLAT
HEAD

ROUND
HEAD

RECESSED,
PHILLIPS HEAD

SLOTTED
HEAD

SHANK

CORE

LENGTH

LAG
SCREW

Fig. 6—2. Kinds of wood screws.

terial, and the type of thread. Common head shapes include flat, round, and oval. They may be slotted for a regular screw driver or hollow for a Phillips type screw driver. Screws are made of steel, stainless steel, brass, bronze, and aluminum, with such finishes as bright, cadmium, copper, brass, blued, nickel, and chromium. The threads vary according to the method for driving. Those designed for use with a screw driver have a thread with less pitch than those to be driven with a hammer (drive screws). The latter are used for quick, permanent installation in soft woods.

Sizes of Wood Screws. Sizes are given by length and by diameter in a gauge number. Common lengths range from ¼″ to 3″ or 4″; diameters range from No. 2 to No. 16. For a flat head screw, the length is over-all; for the round head, it is measured from under the head. The larger the gauge number, the larger the diameter. Is this true for wire brads?

When purchasing wood screws, you will find typical specifications as follows: 1″, No. 8, F.H.B. (flat head bright steel); and 1″, No. 8, R.H.B. (round head blue). Screws are sold in boxes by the gross for the most economical purchase. Be sure to leave the label on the box; it tells the size.

Miscellaneous Screws. The *lag* screw is a heavy-duty wood screw with a square head for a wrench. A washer is used under the head. Length and diameter are given in inches and fractions of inches, respectively. Several kinds of screws are available for hanging and hooking purposes rather than joining woods. These include *screw eyes, screw hooks, cup hooks,* and *shoulder hooks.*

Selecting Wood Screws:

1. First decide on the length and the diameter. In soft woods, a large diameter is necessary for good holding. In hard wood, although adequate for holding, a thin screw may twist off in driving. Steel screws are the strongest.

2. Select the head. Round or oval heads are more decorative than flat ones.

3. Choose the finish or material which seems the most appropriate. Brass or bronze screws are preferred in boat construction, for example.

4. The Phillips head is easier to drive than the slotted, and is also more decorative.

How to Install Wood Screws: Two different-sized holes are always drilled for installing wood screws. A *shank* hole, the size of the screw shank, is drilled in one piece of wood, and a smaller one, the *pilot* hole, or anchor hole, in the other. The screw slips freely through the shank hole, and it cuts threads in the pilot hole as it draws into place. Use as large a diameter screw as will fit the job. It holds better and is less likely to twist off. The shank hole for a flat head screw is *countersunk* so that the top of the head is flush with the surface of the wood (see p. 26).

The round head screw is drawn down snugly, but not enough to damage or distort the wood fibers. The oval head screw is only slightly countersunk.

When you have several screws to install in a board, bore all of the shank holes first, then place the piece in position and mark the pilot holes with an awl. Soap or paraffin can be rubbed on the threads for lubrication in installing.

To *counterbore* the head means to set the head well below the surface. This is done when wooden plugs are to be inserted to conceal the screws.

SOME MISCELLANEOUS FASTENERS

Carriage bolts are designed especially for bolting wooden parts together. The square shoulder under the oval head draws down into the wood to keep the head from turning. Common diameters are ¼", ⁵⁄₁₆", ⅜", and ½". Lengths range from 1" to 6" or more.

Hanger bolts are installed like wood screws, leaving the bolt end for attaching a part.

Toggle bolts are used to fasten wood to hollow walls, or in installations where the nut cannot be reached. The nut folds for inserting into a hole and then springs open so that the bolt can be tightened with a screw driver.

Fig. 6–3 (left). Ways of installing wood screws. Fig. 6–4 (right). A special counterbore drills pilot and shank holes and cuts the counterbore.

Fig. 6–4 Courtesy Stanley Tools

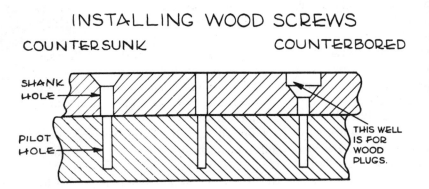

INSTALLING WOOD SCREWS

COUNTERSUNK   COUNTERBORED

SHANK HOLE

PILOT HOLE

THIS WELL IS FOR WOOD PLUGS.

DRILL BIT SIZES FOR WOOD SCREWS

SCREW NUMBER	SHANK DRILL	PILOT DRILL		DIAM. OF COUNTERBORE
		HARDWOOD	SOFTWOOD	
2	3/32	3/64	1/32	3/16
3	7/64	1/16	3/64	1/4
4	7/64	1/16	3/64	1/4
5	1/8	5/64	1/16	1/4
6	9/64	5/64	1/16	5/16
7	5/32	3/32	1/16	5/16
8	11/64	3/32	5/64	3/8
9	3/16	7/64	5/64	3/8
10	3/16	7/64	3/32	3/8
12	7/32	1/8	7/64	7/16
14	1/4	9/64	7/64	1/2

Note: If wood plugs are to be used for decorative purposes, you may prefer to counterbore to a larger diameter than indicated.

BOLTS USED IN WOODWORK

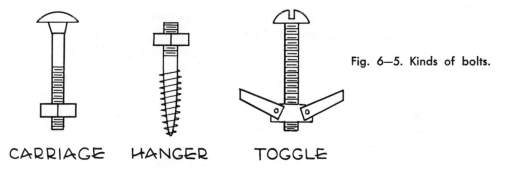

Fig. 6—5. Kinds of bolts.

CARRIAGE   HANGER   TOGGLE

FOR RESEARCH, EXPERIMENT, DEVELOPMENT

1. Why has a screw greater holding power than an unclinched nail?
2. How can nails be driven without splitting the wood?
3. Why would steel woodscrews likely be preferred to aluminum in hard woods?
4. How does one determine the best size of woodscrew to use?
5. Why should the face of the claw hammer be shiny and curved?
6. Why are brass screws preferred in boat construction?
7. How can one tell when to use roundhead or flathead screws?
8. Who is the champion nail driver in your class?
9. Why are gauge numbers used in specifying screw and brad diameters?
10. What is the difference between a carriage bolt and a machine bolt?

chapter 7

USING ADHESIVES

For the finer, more accurate kinds of woodworking, gluing is preferred to other methods of fastening. Any of the wood adhesives is stronger than the wood itself; consequently, a glue joint properly fitted becomes the strongest part. The first essential to good gluing is good joinery—the accurate fitting of parts. Greatest strength results when both pieces are in full contact, with a uniform glue line in between.

All glue joints are made stronger by the pressure of clamping during the setting (see Figures 7-1 and 7-2). The pressure need be only enough to hold the parts in contact. Excessively heavy applications of glue are unnecessary. That which oozes out around the joint should be wiped off immediately with a damp sponge or cloth.

End gluing does not usually produce a sufficiently strong joint to make it practical. However, when the ends butt perfectly together, a remarkably strong joint can be made. A coat of glue is applied to each end and is permitted to penetrate the wood cells by soaking. After a few minutes, depending on the kind of glue used, a second coat is applied and the ends are clamped in place.

Glues that require mixing before using should be mixed strictly according to the recommendations of the manufacturer, who knows how to get the greatest strength with his product. It is recommended that glues be used at not less than room temperature. Heat hastens setting; heat lamps may be used when necessary.

Re-Gluing. Whenever a glue joint must be re-glued, as in the case of making repairs, the selection of the glue is very important. It is necessary to remove the old glue, but it may be impossible to get it out of the pores without cutting away some of the wood. When this is not feasible, water soluble glues are not recommended for re-gluing. Use plastics adhesives; they will adhere to non-porous surfaces better.

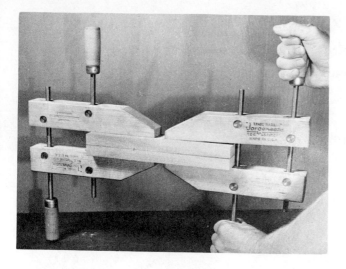

Fig. 7—1. The jaws of the hand screw clamp must be in full contact with the stock for the best clamping.

CEMENTS

Contact Cements. Contact cements are used when bonding veneers and resin laminates to wood. After a uniform coating has been applied to each side, the cement is allowed to dry for 30 to 40 minutes. The pieces are then placed together and pressed by a heavy roller. It is necessary that the coated surfaces be properly positioned before touching. Once in contact, they cannot be moved. A good method for bonding large areas is to place a piece of wrapping paper between the two cemented surfaces.

When they are properly positioned, carefully withdraw the paper.

Plastics Cements. Plastics cements are available usually in tubes, for example, model airplane cement. They dry so quickly that they are most suitable when the glue area is not large. These cements are waterproof and hard when dry, and are especially useful when making repairs. Epoxy resin cement, a fairly recent development, is considered the strongest of adhesives. It is mixed before using. Follow the instructions on the container carefully.

Fig. 7—2. Alternate the end grain in glued-up sections.

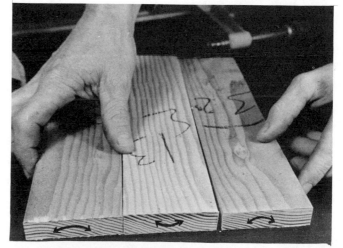

A READY-REFERENCE CHART ON GLUES AND GLUING
(Courtesy Franklin Glue Company)

GLUE TYPE	ROOM TEMPERATURE	HOW TO PREPARE	HOW TO APPLY	70° CLAMPING TIME
Liquid hide	Sets above 70°. Can be used in colder room if glue is warmer.	Ready for use.	Apply thin coat on both surfaces; let get tacky before joining.	3 hours
Flake or powdered animal	Must be 70° or warmer. Keep work warm.	For each ounce glue add 1½ ounces water (softwoods) or 2 ounces (hardwood)	Apply heavy coat at 140° to both surfaces. Assemble quickly before glue chills.	1½ hours
White liquid resin	Any temperature above 60°, but the warmer the better.	Ready to use.	Spread on at once, and clamp at once.	1½ hours
Resorcinol	Must be 70° or warmer. Will set faster at 90°.	Mix 3 parts powder to 4 parts liquid catalyst.	Apply thin coat to both surfaces. Use within 8 hours after mixing.	16 hours
Powdered resin	Must be 70° or warmer. Will set faster at 90°.	Mix 2 parts powder with ½ to 1 part water.	Apply thin coat to both surfaces. Use within 4 hours after mixing.	16 hours
Powdered casein	Any temperature above freezing, but the warmer the better.	Stir together equal parts by volume of glue and water. Wait 10 minutes and stir again.	Apply thin coat to both surfaces. Use within 8 hours after mixing.	2 hours
Aliphatic resin	As low as 50°.	Ready to use.	Spread and clamp immediately.	1½ hours

ESPECIALLY GOOD FOR	NOT SO GOOD FOR	ADVANTAGES
Furniture, cabinet work, and general gluing.	It is not waterproof. Do not use on boats, outdoor furniture, etc.	Very strong, tough, and not brittle. Convenient to use. Has good filling qualities. Gives strength even in poorly fitting joints.
Quantity woodwork jobs and with expert gluers.	Not waterproof. Too much trouble to make.	Same advantages as for liquid hide glue when properly used. Least expensive.
All-around household glue.	Not moisture resistant. Not as strong as hide glue on furniture.	Always ready to use at any temperature. Quick setting. Can be used without clamps.
For any woodworking that may be exposed to soaking.	Not good at temperatures lower than 70°. Because of dark color it is used only when the joint must be waterproof.	Very strong, waterproof. Works well with poor joints.
For woodworking and general gluing where considerable moisture resistance is desired.	Not for use on oily woods. Joints must fit tightly and be securely clamped.	Very strong, but brittle if joint fits poorly. Almost waterproof.
For most woodworking jobs. Especially good with oily woods: cypress, lemon, etc.	Not moisture resistant. Will stain some woods.	Strong. Works in cool locations. Fills poorly fitting joints.
All-around glue for wood.	Not waterproof.	Stronger than white liquid resins. Better heat and solvent resistance. Nonstaining.

GLUING UP TOPS

When table and bench tops and other large pieces are constructed of solid wood, there are three items of major concern:

1. To make the top so that it will stay flat.
2. To get the most permanent glue joints.
3. To obtain a maximum of strength and ability to absorb shock, as is needed in bench tops, lids, and doors.

The following suggestions will help in obtaining the desired results:

To Keep a Top Flat:

1. Start with flat, true stock.
2. Alternate the end grain of each piece.
3. Use narrow pieces in preference to wide.
4. Make plow cuts on the circular saw,

halfway through the thickness on the under side of the board on which you are working. Space them about 2" apart.

5. Use the same number of clamps on each side of the assembly to assure even compression.

To Secure Maximum Strength:

1. Glue narrow strips together, alternating the grain, with the edge grain up.
2. Through bolts or dowels may be installed.

To Get the Best Glue Joints:

1. When assembling several pieces at one time, get a buddy to help.
2. Cut pieces from the same board.
3. Equalize clamping pressure to prevent distorting the stock.
4. Accurate fitting of the edges in full contact is necessary for maximum

Fig. 7—3. A wedge jig for miter gluing.

Courtesy Franklin Glue Company

Courtesy Franklin Glue Company

Fig. 7—4 (left). A wedge jig for gluing splined miters. Fig. 7—5 (right). A simple clamping jig for edge gluing.

strength in any joint you make.

5. Use a glue recommended for that purpose.
6. Let glue set at room temperature.
7. Do not remove the clamps too soon.

Cleaning Up. To save work and time, cover the bench or the floor area with old newspapers to catch any glue drippings. Clean off any glue in clamps or tools before it hardens.

FOR RESEARCH, EXPERIMENT, DEVELOPMENT

1. Why can a glue joint be stronger than the wood surrounding it?
2. Why is it more difficult to get a strong bond when re-gluing a joint?
3. Why will a table top of narrow strips usually warp less than one made of wide boards?
4. Which types of adhesives would be preferred for laminating?
5. How can one tell when the clamps can safely be removed?
6. Why is an end grain glue joint not as strong as the wood itself, while an edge to edge joint is stronger than the wood?
7. Why is a thin layer of a glue in a joint stronger than a thick layer?
8. Why does glue not fill up gaps in a poorly fitting joint?
9. Why are glue joints involving different kinds of wood likely to crack?
10. Why is laminated wood stronger than solid wood of the same kind and cross sectional area?

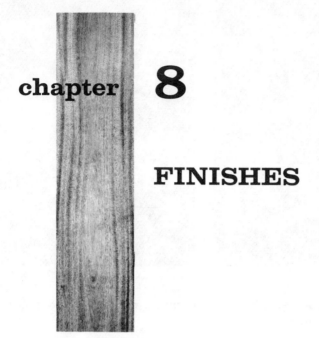

chapter 8

FINISHES

Products and projects of wood usually need protection from wear, soiling, staining, moisture, weather, or heat. Finishes provide such protection. The natural beauty of wood can be enhanced as well as protected by the finish. A smooth easy-to-clean surface on wood is obtained by the application of an appropriate finish. A smooth finish on a model airplane or soap box racer cuts down air resistance. Thus, finishes serve several purposes, and there are a great many finishing materials available to serve these purposes.

The finishes used by the early cabinet makers included such natural waxes as tallow and beeswax, shellac and linseed oil. Melted pitch and rosin were used on boats. Discovery of other waxes, oils, and rosins made varnish and enamels possible. Chemistry now has produced a group of finishing materials called *synthetics* which are generally superior to the natural materials (see p. 108). The new plastic finishes now available suggest that in the future all finishing materials will probably originate in chemists' test tubes.

Whatever the finishing material used, remember that a good finishing job improves any project, while a poor one spoils even the best project.

TYPES OF FINISHES

Finishes for woods can be classified according to the effects desired.

1. Clear, transparent finishes: Clear

lacquers, white shellac, clear varnishes, oil, waxes, and plastics.

2. Colored, transparent finishes: Transparent lacquers, orange shellac, stains, varnish stains, color waxes.

3. Opaque finishes: Tempera, enamels, lacquers, paints.

4. Waterproof, weather-resistant finishes: Lacquer, spar varnish, enamels, plastics.

5. Penetrating finishes: Oils, stains, sealers.

6. Plastic finishes.

7. Novelty finishes: Crystal, texture, bleach, chemical vapor.

SHELLAC FINISHES

A shellac finish has the advantage of easy application by brush, dip, or spray. It is quick drying and has good sealing qualities. However, it is stained and softened with water, gets sticky with heat, and scratches easily. It can be used as an appropriate finish on projects that are not exposed to moisture, handling, or rough use. It is not recommended for table tops, floors, work benches, and the like. A shellac finish needs the protection of several coats of polishing wax.

A thin coat of shellac, called a wash coat, makes a good sealer for soft woods such as basswood and white pine. Use it before applying tempera or enamel. For the best results shellac should be applied in thin coats. Dilute it as much as 1:1 with wood alcohol or shellac solvent. It then dries dust-free in a few minutes. If used full strength, it will remain sticky for several days and may never actually dry. Several thin coats, as many as five or more, are needed to build up enough thickness for rubbing and polishing. Sand between coats with very fine sandpaper.

Shellac brushes are easy to clean. Rinse them well in the solvent and let them dry. If a brush is not cleaned, it dries hard. But it can be reclaimed by soaking in the solvent. Remove shellac from clothing with the alcohol solvent.

LACQUER FINISHES

Lacquers are widely used as industrial finishes and are proving to be especially fine on wood furniture. Most lacquers are sprayed on because they dry so rapidly. They are dust-free in a few minutes, waterproof, and available in clear transparent, opaque and transparent colors, and in glossy or dull surfaces.

Brushing lacquers dry more slowly than those used for spraying or dipping. The solvents are called lacquer thinners or reducers. Those for spraying are more volatile than those for brushing. It is important to use the thinner recommended by the manufacturer of the lacquer.

Lacquer should be applied in thin coats for best results. A thick coat will dry quickly on the outside, preventing the inside from drying, with the result that it will stay soft for days. No rubbing between coats is necessary unless there are runs, because each coat dissolves the one beneath it.

A coat of lacquer sealer is first applied to wood. When dry, it is sanded smooth to provide a nonabsorbent surface. On open porous wood use a filler under the sealer. Sand the filled surface before sealing.

Brush application can be successful if the lacquer is flowed on, not brushed out. Thin the lacquer until it is only a little heavier than milk. Apply ten or more coats, and, as a final coat, use the solvent alone. When spraying, use the

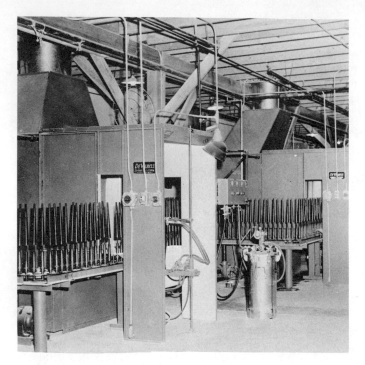

Fig. 8—1. Industry applies finishes automatically. Here table legs are being sprayed automatically at the rate of 840 pieces per hour.

Courtesy DeVilbiss Company and Riverside Furniture Company

solvent for the final coat also. The final polishing is done with lacquer rubbing compound.

If lacquer is applied over varnish or enamel, a blistering results. Varnish and enamels can, however, be applied over lacquer. Actually the lacquer solvents are so strong that they are used for paint removers.

Brushes should be rinsed in the thinner until clean. If kept for lacquer only, no washing in soap and water is necessary. Use the thinner sparingly to remove lacquer from the hands and clothing.

VARNISH AND ENAMEL FINISHES

Varnish and enamel are essentially the same, except that enamel has pigment and varnish is clear. These finishes usually dry more slowly than lacquers, but some synthetics dry as quickly. Enamels are durable and waterproof, and are easy to apply with a brush. Spraying is difficult with slow drying types because of the tendency to run.

When enamels and varnishes are applied, they build up in distinct layers, coat by coat. They do not dissolve together as lacquers do. Each coat should be sanded smooth before the next is applied. It is usually necessary that they dry overnight, at least before sanding. Rubbing out a varnish produces a beautifully rich surface with a dull sheen. This is a very slow process and is rarely used in industry today. A dull varnish applied as the last coat can give the same effect. Glossy varnishes and enamels are usually more durable and waterproof, and easier to keep clean than the dull.

When applying varnishes and enamels with a brush, it is best not to thin them. They are chemically balanced in manufacture and adding thinner may upset this balance. If a thinner should be necessary, use only that recommended on the label. Apply the coats just heavy enough to make them self-leveling, leaving no brush marks. On soft woods, a sealer or priming coat is recommended. Special undercoats are available for enamels.

Dust is usually a problem with slow-drying finishes. In fact, unless you have a special room where dust can be controlled, you will not get a really smooth finish. Spraying the floor with water will help to eliminate dust.

Enamel and varnish brushes should be rinsed in the solvent, then washed in hot soapy water and wrapped in wax paper so that they will not collect dust. To remove these finishes from hands and clothing, use the same solvent before the varnish or enamel has dried.

Wax should not be applied to varnish or enamel until it is thoroughly dry, otherwise the wax may dissolve the surface and spoil the finish. It is often not safe to apply wax sooner than two or three weeks.

VARNISH STAINS

Varnish stains are finishes in which stain has been added to clear varnish. They are applied as though they were varnish and they are intended to stain and varnish in one operation. For best results on your projects, however, use stain and varnish separately.

WAX FINISHES

Waxes alone can produce beautiful, durable finishes—alone, that is, except for rubbing. It takes much rubbing to bring out the characteristic dull luster. The paste form of wax is preferred. It may be of the type used for furniture, for automobiles, or for shoes. The wood should be sanded as smoothly as possible if a luster is desired.

Fig. 8—2 (left). When varnish is brushed on, apply the coat in the direction of the grain. Brush from the center to the ends of the surface. Fig. 8—3 (right). Level the varnish by brushing it across the grain.

Courtesy Sherwin-Williams Company

Put the wax inside a cloth pad and rub it over the surface. The wax will filter through the cloth leaving a residue behind. This technique saves rubbing; try it when waxing the car, too. After each coat is dry, rub it energetically with a soft cloth or a piece of sheepskin. A soft buff on a portable electric drill makes the rubbing easier. The heat produced by the friction of rubbing helps the wax to penetrate. Four or five coats will give a good finish which does not scratch. It is easily maintained, too.

A coating of wax protects any finish and makes dust removal easier. Remember, however, that the only finish that can be applied over wax is more wax. Nothing else will adhere to it.

TEMPERA COLORS

Tempera is a water-mixed opaque color commonly used for posters and show cards. It works well for painted or stenciled decoration on wood projects, such as toys and novelties. First apply a wash coat of shellac and when dry, sand it lightly to remove any gloss. Apply only one coat of tempera; two or more will usually peel. When dry, apply a coat of clear lacquer over the surface to make the tempera permanent. Spraying is recommended, although if the lacquer is laid on carefully with a brush, the colors do not bleed.

It is much easier to paint details on with tempera than with enamels, and when protected with lacquer they are durable. Use Speedball pens for fine lines. Thin the tempera with water so that it will feed through the pen points. India ink can be used in the same manner.

WOOD FILLER

All woods are porous, some more than others. If a very smooth finish is desired, it is necessary that these pores be filled level with the rest of the surface. On such close-grained woods as cherry, maple, and birch, a wash coat of shellac, a sealer

Fig. 8—4 (left). Wood filler is mixed to a thick creamy consistency and brushed into the wood with a stiff brush. Fig. 8—5. When the filler coat begins to take on a dull appearance, wipe it off across the grain. Use paper towels first, and then cloths.

Courtesy Sherwin-Williams Company

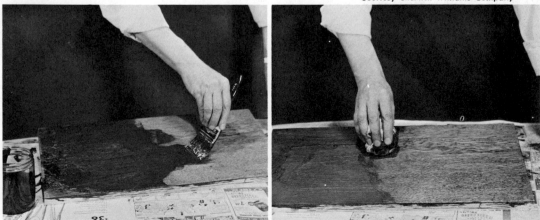

coat, or a coat of linseed oil thinned with turpentine may be sufficient.

Open grain woods such as walnut, mahogany, and oak need a paste wood filler. This is a thick, creamy mixture of silex, linseed oil, thinner, and drier. Oil stain is added so that both filling and staining can be done at once. Filler without stain is called *natural*.

Apply a thick coating of the desired filler and pack it into the pores with a stiff brush. As soon as it has dried dull, wipe off the excess with burlap, excelsior, or crumpled newspaper. Wipe *across the grain* so that the filler is not removed from the pores. Cover only a small area at a time because the filler dries quickly and then is difficult to wipe off. After it has dried overnight, sand the surface with fine sandpaper to remove any muddy appearance. Then it is ready for the rest of the finish. Apply a lacquer sealer first if the finish is to be lacquer. For balsa wood models, you can make your own fillers. Add whiting, available at the hardware store, to whatever color of lacquer you plan to use. A half cup of whiting to a half pint of lacquer is adequate. Apply as many coats as are needed to make a smooth surface, sanding between each.

WOOD STAINS

The color of a wood can be changed by the application of a stain. Only the color is changed, not the grain pattern. You may not believe in staining one wood to resemble another, and yet you may find use for the stain. A streak of sap wood can be easily stained to match the heart wood. In case you do not wish to dye the sap wood, you may still prefer a wood filler to which stain has been added.

The most common types of wood stains are the *oil* and the *water*. Oil stains are diluted with turpentine or paint thinner and are easier to apply than water wood stains. They can be applied with brush, rag, or sponge and give little streaking. To keep the end grain from becoming too dark, since it will soak up stain like a sponge, apply a coat of linseed oil to the end grain just before staining. As soon as the stain coat has been applied, wipe it thoroughly with a cloth to get the best blending. One coat is usually sufficient.

Courtesy Sherwin-Williams Company

Fig. 8—6 (above). Oil stain is brushed on. Fig. 8—7 (below). For uniform staining, wipe off oil stain before it dries. Spraying is better for large areas.

Water stains penetrate deeply and are the most economical to use. The dye is mixed in water and is best applied with brush or sponge, although on large areas spray is recommended. Upon drying, the wood surface is rough because of the swelling effect of the water. It must be sanded before proceeding. Dilute the mixture further for the end grain. Be careful not to sand through the stain on the edges and corners.

Stains are usually applied before other finishing materials. A simple, but effective stain-type finish can be gotten with enamels. Apply a heavy, runny coat and immediately rub it in and wipe it off with a cloth. When dry, steel wool the surface lightly, and wax. Always try out stains on scrap pieces of the same wood to test the color effect. Stains alone are not complete finishes. They are covered with other transparent finishes such as varnish, shellac, lacquer, or wax. If clear lacquer is to be applied over an oil stain, it is necessary to first protect the stain with a coat of lacquer sealer to prevent an undesirable chemical reaction.

PENETRATING FINISHES

Oil finishes penetrate deeply into the wood and consequently produce a different effect than those that remain on the surface, such as varnishes and lacquer. It takes a penetrating finish to bring out the full beauty of grain figure and color. A mixture of warm linseed oil and turpentine is still preferred by many woodworkers. When mixed to the proportions of 1:1, and heated, this solution is readily absorbed in the wood. Swab on each coat heavily and let it soak in for about an hour. Then wipe off the excess and let it dry overnight. Rub it well with a soft cloth before applying

another coat. Rubbing is necessary to bring out the beauty, and it seems that the more coats, the more beautiful the finish. Four or five, however, are usually sufficient. This finish must be protected by wax.

Prepared penetrating finishes are available. They are complete finishes containing oils, resins, and waxes which give durability as well as beauty. The seal used on wood floors in gymnasiums is such a finish. This type is excellent for furniture, too. Dust is of little concern, because the excess liquid is wiped off after about thirty minutes. When dry, the surface is rubbed with fine steel wool and a second coat is applied. This must be applied very thin or it will remain tacky for days. Two coats are usually adequate. Because there are so many brands of these finishes, follow the manufacturer's instructions for use.

Clean brushes in the recommended thinner, and then wash in hot, soapy water.

PLASTICS FINISHES

There are many plastics finishes available which, when properly applied, make unusually durable surface coatings. It is important to study the manufacturer's instructions. Some of the finishes require a catalyst for setting; others are self-curing. They can be flowed on, brushed, dipped, and sprayed. The fumes are usually inflammable and should not be inhaled. Be sure to provide plenty of ventilation when using them.

MISCELLANEOUS FINISHING MATERIALS

The term *paint* is a general one, which to most people includes all finishing materials such as enamels, varnishes, lacquers, and house paint. With the great assortment of finishes available today, however, paints are now only one type of finish. They are used for the exterior and interior of buildings, including houses. Paints are mixtures of oils, emulsions, pigments, and driers. Enamels, in contrast, are made of synthetic or natural varnish, plus pigments.

Linseed oil is one of the most useful of ingredients. Extracted from the seed of flax, it adds elasticity and durability to finishes. In house paint it withstands weather well. *Raw* linseed oil is used in exterior paints. *Boiled* linseed oil is preferred for interiors and furniture finishes. It can be thinned with turpentine or paint thinner.

Turpentine—a favorite thinner for paints, enamels, and varnishes—is made from the sap of southern yellow pine. It is clear, colorless, oily, and has a distinct yellow pine odor that bothers some people. Numerous turpentine substitutes are manufactured from petroleum. They have less objectionable odors and are often recommended in place of turpentine. As a group, these are called *paint thinners* and *mineral spirits*. To determine the proper thinner, read the label on the can of finish you are using.

Tinting colors are pigments ground in linseed oil. Made in a great many colors, they are added to varnish or enamels to change the basic color. Tinting colors are very intense and must be stirred well into the finish.

Bleaches are chemicals for removing color from wood. The so-called blonde mahogany has been bleached. Prepared bleaches are recommended, and the directions should be followed explicitly.

Crack fillers, wood putty, and *plastic woods* are useful when cracks, dents, holes, and other such defects cannot be removed. There are many brands from which to choose. Some will take stains, and some will not. It is generally best to fill large cavities a little at a time, letting one layer dry before adding the next. Allowance should be made for shrinkage;

Courtesy Sherwin-Williams Company

Fig. 8—8 (left). Applying a bleach with a sponge. Note the rubber gloves to protect the skin.

Fig. 8—9 (right). Mahogany before and after bleaching.

apply the filler slightly higher than the surrounding surface and, when dry, sand it level.

Stick shellac, available in many colors to match finished woods, is melted into the cavity with a hot knife. Then it is sanded level with the surface.

Masking tape is very helpful in painting straight lines and designs, and for holding protective paper over parts of a project while spray painting.

NOVELTY FINISHES

There are many unusual finishing treatments that are appropriate now and then. It is important to use them only when they are in the interests of good design and good taste.

The *sugi* finish originated with a Japanese wood, sugi, which is used for decorative work after it has been weathered and worn, much as driftwood is weathered in the sea. Those woods which have a marked difference between springwood and summerwood, such as Douglas fir, yellow pine, oak, and cypress, can be treated to resemble the original sugi. A blow torch is used to char the soft areas and then this is removed with a wire brush, brushing in the direction of the grain. Oil or wax is then applied.

A *sandblast* finish gives an effect similar to sugi, except that there is no discoloration due to the burning. Sandblasted fir panel is available at lumber dealers.

Texture paints used for interior walls can be applied to wood projects. They are thick and plastic and can be given an endless variety of textures, by means of sponging, finger painting, stippling, troweling with a putty knife, and so forth.

Crystalline finishes are applied like enamels or lacquers by brush, dip, or spray. Some of them on drying develop a fine network of wrinkles, and some develop crystals. Some are heated in an oven to produce the crystallization.

Burnishing produces rich lusters without the use of any finishing material. The wood is energetically rubbed with a piece of wood and gradually the surface becomes smooth and glossy. It is used for especially beautiful effects on fine hardwood sculpture and carvings.

APPLICATION OF FINISHES

It is only the properly applied, appropriate finish that serves the two basic purposes of surface coatings: protection and decoration. The preparation of the wood surface for the finish is fully as important as is the actual application. When the final sanding is complete, the surface should be dampened with a sponge and water. On drying, the wood will be roughened due to the raising of the fibers. A light sanding removes this roughness. When the project is allowed to stand for several days after this treatment and before finishing, it may be necessary to re-sand it, because atmospheric moisture tends to raise the grain.

Immediately before the finish is applied, the project should be vacuum-brushed to remove all dust. Then it should be wiped with a "tack rag." This is a lintless cloth dampened with the solvent for the finish being used.

All pigmented finishes should be stirred thoroughly before using and frequently during the application to assure a uniform coloring. Stirring should be done in such a way that no air is whipped into the paint. Bubbles leave the surface rough unless picked up immediately.

All paints should be strained just before using to catch any clots, bubbles, bits of film, and foreign matter. Special disposable strainers are available at paint stores.

Always wipe the paint out of the paintwell around the opening in the container before replacing the lid. Set the can on the floor and step the lid down securely to keep air from the paint.

Dipping. For small parts such as details on models and pieces that might be turned out in a production project, dipping is a quick, effective method of painting. It works best with quick drying enamels and lacquers. With the part suspended on an improvised hook, dip it, drain for a few seconds, scrape off any excess on the bottom, and hang it up to dry. The problems, if any, are those of devising hooks to hold the parts. The paint should be as thick as it comes from the can.

Brushing and Brushes. Brushes are commonly classed as enamel and varnish brushes, wall brushes, and artists' brushes. In addition, there are those for special purposes, such as sash brushes, striping brushes, stencil brushes, and glue brushes. The bristles are usually animal hair set in rubber and held by a metal ferrule. Hog bristles, squirrel, ox, and camel hair are used in less expensive brushes, while wild boar bristles from China and red sable hair from Europe are used in the better ones. Bristles of plastics, such as nylon, are being used in wall brushes. The longer the bristles and the thicker they are set, the more paint the brush will hold. This capacity is important for smooth coats of enamel and lacquer. Short bristle brushes are too stiff, and leave many brush marks.

Because it pays to use good brushes, it also pays to take good care of them.

When it is necessary to clean a brush, do it immediately after using it. First rinse the brush in the proper solvent. Then, with hot water and a sudsy soap or detergent, wash out all traces of color. Give it a final rinse and wrap it in waxed paper or aluminum foil to keep it dust free. When the brush is not to be cleaned, its paint should be kept moist. Drill a hole through the handle and hang it in a container of the solvent. Do not let the bristles rest on the bottom, or they will curl out of shape.

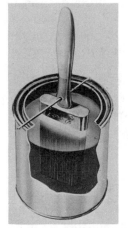

Fig. 8–10. A simple brush holder.

When shellac, lacquer, and tempera harden in a brush, they can be softened with the respective solvent. When enamel and varnish harden, cleaning is a chore. Lacquer thinner or any one of the many available prepared brush cleaners can be used to soften enamel. Be sure to rinse the brush well and wash with soap and water.

Brushing. An expert with a brush can apply a finish as smoothly as it can be sprayed, but brushing is not as simple as it might appear. Study these suggestions.

1. The finish should preferably be strained after thorough mixing. Pour a quantity into a clean container instead of using it from the can.
2. Immediately before using a brush, rinse it in the proper solvent. This makes the brush easier to clean.
3. Use as large a brush as you can handle. A beginner usually picks too small a brush, assuming that it is easier to control. It is difficult to achieve smooth coatings with small brushes.
4. Dip the brush deep in the finish to get a full load. Then scrape off the excess on the edge of the container.
5. Lay the work out horizontally when possible; it is easier to get an even coating.
6. When feasible, leave the piece in a horizontal position until it is dry enough that it cannot run.
7. To get a smooth coat on a vertical surface, brush vertically, not horizontally, and pick up the runs with the tip of the brush as soon as they appear. After five minutes of drying, it will probably be too late to pick up a run.
8. Starting at the center and near an edge, lay the brush nearly flat on its bristles and draw it slowly toward the end or edge, preferably in the direction of the grain. As soon as the brush shows signs of running out of paint, dip it again.
9. Now start at the center again, brushing in the opposite direction, and complete the stroke. Repeat this with a slight overlapping of strokes.
10. Shellac and lacquer must be used very thin. Enamels and varnishes are applied heavily so that they will level themselves out and eliminate brush marks. Too much brushing and stretching of the finish produces a rough surface.
11. Most enamels will cover well in one coat, providing they are not brushed out too thin. On the other hand, an excessively heavy coat will dry too slowly and will collect more dust and finger marks.
12. Pick up any hairs or air bubbles with the tip of the brush immediately.
13. Take the necessary precautions against dust and against those people who must test the freshness of paint with their fingers. What to do about the fingers may be a "touchy" problem.

SPRAY FINISHES

Spraying is the accepted industrial method for most applications of finishes. The development of quick-drying materials and the use of infrared heat for drying makes spray finishing fast and economical. Uniform application is most easily obtained, especially when spraying is done automatically. The finishing material is thinned with the proper solvent so that it can be easily broken up into a fine mist. Air pressures used vary from about 30-60 pounds, depending on the spray material. The goal in spraying is a uniformly even coating, and this is built up with several thin applications rather than with one thick one.

Spray Equipment. A good spray gun with an adequate supply of air, and an exhaust system are the essential items of equipment for spraying. There are two basic types of guns: the *pressure feed* and the *suction feed*. The first is so constructed that pressure in the container forces the material through the nozzle where it is atomized. This gun is used for the heavy, slow-drying finishes. The suction feed gun has the spray material exposed to atmospheric pressure; as the air is forced through the gun it induces a partial vacuum, the atmospheric pressure then forcing the material into the nozzle where it is atomized. Spray guns may be of the *internal* or *external* mix types, depending on whether the material is broken up inside or outside the nozzle. *Bleeder* guns permit passage of air through the gun at all times, whether or not spraying is being done.

An adequate quantity of air is as necessary as adequate air pressure. Many types of air compressors are available for either home or school use. Some use a piston and cylinder for compressing; some, the diaphragm; and some, the blower. Variation in air pressure is obtained by a pressure regulator operating by means of an adjustable diaphragm.

Using a Spray Gun. Spraying looks simple and sure; you probably won't find any difficulties until you try it. However, with an equal amount of study and practice, you can probably do a more professional job of painting with a spray gun than with a brush. Follow these suggestions.

1. Wipe the surface with a tack rag just before spraying.
2. Thin the spray material until it can be sprayed in a fine, even mist without spattering or sputtering. Always strain it through a fine screen or a disposable strainer. Set the nozzle for a fan spray. Adjust the air pressure if necessary.
3. Although it is not always possible, it is desirable to have enough material in the gun to complete one coat.
4. With the object to be painted in the spray booth and the exhaust fan in operation, hold the gun horizontally with the nozzle 10 to 12 inches away from the surface. The nozzle should be directed beyond the right or left edge of the piece. Press the trigger. This starts the spray just before the gun passes across the edge and assures an even coating.
5. Move the spray across the surface past the opposite end and release the trigger. This is the basic spray stroke that is repeated until the coating is complete. The nozzle must be held at a uniform distance from the work to produce a uniform coat. This is the tricky part of spraying. Hold the gun fixed in a comfortable position and

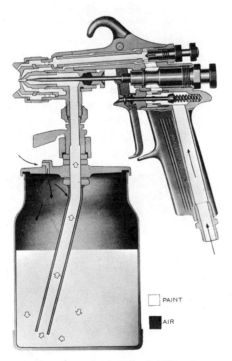

PAINT

AIR

Courtesy The DeVilbiss Company

Fig. 8—11. The interior of a spray gun.

Fig. 8—12. Paint and varnish remover is applied with a brush, and after a few minutes the softened finish is scraped off.

Courtesy Sherwin-Williams Company

rock back and forth from side to side keeping your feet in place. You can make a sort of machine out of your body this way. If you sweep your arm from side to side, the gun will travel in an arc, spraying the paint on thin at the ends and thick in the middle.

6. Several thin coats are better than a thick one. When they are thin, there is little trouble with runs.

7. Should runs occur, you have two choices: first, wipe them off with a clean cloth dipped in solvent; second, let them dry and sand them. The former is often preferred if only a coat or two have been applied. When it is the last coat that runs, it is better to let it dry and then rub it out.

Fig. 8—13. Paint remover can be applied in hard-to-reach places with a tooth-brush.

Courtesy Sherwin-Williams Company

Courtesy Sherwin-Williams Company

Fig. 8—14. All traces of the paint remover must be thoroughly removed from the wood before the finish is applied. Use the proper solvent as recommended by the manufacturer.

Spray Gun Care. A clogged, dirty gun is as useless as a hard paint brush. Clogging need not happen if the container is rinsed immediately after use and the solvent is sprayed through the gun. Remember, this solvent may be very inflammable. If so, spray it out the exhaust vent. If someone forgets to clean the gun, it is hoped that he will get the job of reclaiming it, which usually takes hours.

REFINISHING

The problems in removing an old finish and applying a new one vary from job to job. There are certain general recommendations to follow, however.

Old finish can be removed by scraping, sanding, heating, and dissolving. If the project is of solid wood, scraping, planing, or even heating may be possible. On a veneer surface only sanding and dissolving should be used. Extremely thick coating can be quickly removed with an electric paint remover. This is a device for applying enough heat to soften the coats for easy scraping. Burning with a flame is hazardous, especially because most finishing materials are inflammable.

The prepared paint and varnish removers are strong solvents to be brushed on heavily and allowed to react. The softened finish is then scraped off. This may be repeated until the bare wood has been reached. Most of these removers irritate the skin; rubber gloves are recommended. Lye solution, although effective in removing paint, should not be used in the school shop. The danger of severe burns is too great. Be sure to remove the solution from the wood with the rinse recommended by the manufacturer.

It is difficult to remove finish from down in the pores of the wood. Planing off a thin shaving may be the answer. When removing a finish with sandpaper, use a coarse grade because the finish clogs a fine paper. Flint paper is recommended. Turned pieces can be most easily sanded on the wood lathe.

When the old finish has been completely removed, the new is applied as though it were the first. Sometimes it is desirable to take the piece apart to facilitate the work. When glue joints are broken, this is usually a good idea.

 **SAFETY SENSE**

1. Spray painting produces fumes that should not be inhaled; nor should the paint mist be drawn into the lungs. An adequate ventilating and exhaust system is necessary for the protection of the operator and to eliminate the hazard of a fire.

2. If the exhaust system is not adequate to control the mist, the operator should wear a respirator.

3. When painting in a room, the doors and windows should be open and a fan should be used to draw out the fumes. Odors of some paints are objectionable to some people, as well as dangerous.

4. Finish-soaked wiping cloths and paper towels must be disposed of immediately, or kept in safety waste cans for later disposal. They are so inflammable that they can ignite by themselves under certain conditions.

5. All finishing materials should be kept in metal containers, stored in metal cabinets. In a well-planned finishing room, the lights will have explosion-proof fixtures and non-arcing switches.

6. Cleanliness and safety go hand-in-hand in the finishing room. Cleanliness and quality of finish are close relatives, too, so cleanliness makes extra good sense.

FOR RESEARCH, EXPERIMENT, DEVELOPMENT

1. Why do synthetic finishes tend to be better than natural finishes?
2. Why do oil finishes reveal a different quality of beauty in a wood than surface finishes do?
3. Why do shellac finishes need further protection?
4. Why do lacquer finishes dry quickly?
5. Why will paint thinner not soften a brush left to harden in enamel?
6. Why is a large brush preferred to a small one for finishing?
7. Why may novelty finishes soon become tiresome?
8. How is dust controlled for finishing?
9. How can one tell when a spray coating is sufficiently thick?
10. Why must a spray gun be cleaned immediately after using?

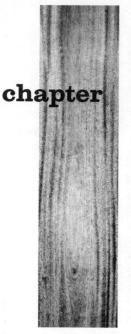

chapter 9

UPHOLSTERY

Upholstery is one of the highly skilled activities in furniture manufacturing. The conventional methods require hand work almost exclusively. However, along with the simpler, more functional design and construction of contemporary furniture, simpler methods for upholstering have been developed. The introduction of foam rubber and plastics has simplified the processes and at the same time has made upholstery more comfortable, durable, and less costly. Foam cushioning requires no elaborate built-up spring suspension, nor layers of padding to support it. In its simplest forms it requires only fabric covering. Foam has its comfort and resiliency built in.

Conventional springing can be used if desired, and when cushioned with foam it is extra comfortable. However, since foam can be cemented directly to a solid base with such desirable results, the built-up construction is superfluous for many uses.

URETHANE FOAMS

The newest foam materials for use in upholstery are plastic products called *urethanes*. There are two types. Polyester, the stiffer, is used mostly for sponges, garment liners, and insulation. The polyether urethanes are used for cushioning. The latter material is available in the same forms as foam rubber. The pincore types have largely replaced the earlier forms, which had large core holes. Pincores are deep, small diameter holes.

There is some difference of opinion over the comparative qualities of the foam rubber and foam plastic. These materials are not completely interchangeable. This means that each has advantages for particular installations. Urethane is available from many manufacturers and in a variety of specifications. It is noticeably lighter in weight than the rubber foam, weighing only

Fig. 9—1. Liquid latex is poured into molds to cure.

Courtesy Goodyear Tire and Rubber Company

one-third to one-half as much. Consult a particular manufacturer's specifications for the qualities you want, and for the adhesive recommended. Both foams are handled in the same manner for cushioning.

HOW FOAM RUBBER IS MADE

The liquid latex is blended to a special formula and whipped into an air-filled froth, like meringue on a lemon pie, and poured into molds for curing. It becomes a one-piece form made up of millions of tiny latex-walled air cells.

TYPES OF FOAM RUBBER STOCK

Foam rubber is available in several forms and degrees of softness. The *slab utility* stock comes in thicknesses from ¼" to 2", in slabs 54" x 44", and in 54" rolls. *Flat utility* stock has hollow core construction and is made in thicknesses from 1" to 4½". The coring makes the cushion more cushioning and resilient. *Full-molded* cushions employ core construction and require covering only with upholstery fabric. They are available in many sizes.

Compression Ranges. The softness or firmness of foam rubber is specified as *compression.* The range of compressions for slab stock include:

X Soft,	5–10 lbs.	X Firm,	60– 85 lbs.
Soft,	10–25 lbs.	XX Firm,	85–115 lbs.
Medium,	25–40 lbs.	XXX Firm,	115–150 lbs.
Firm,	40–60 lbs.	XXXX Firm,	150–200 lbs.

The weights given above refer to the weight required to compress the thickness 25 per cent.

Cored flat stock is available in No. 3, 22-35 lbs; No. 4, 35-50 lbs; and No. 5, 50-67 lbs.

The ranges for molded cushions are No. 1 for backs over flexible springing; No. 2 for seats over flexible springing; and No. 3 for use over solid bases.

USING FOAM RUBBER AND URETHANE

Foam is easily cut with upholsterer's scissors or on the band saw. When band sawing, place foam on a piece of wrapping paper to permit it to slide easily over the table. When using scissors on heavy stock, dip them in water occasionally for lubrication. Edges and corners can be rounded with the scissors and the roughness buffed or sanded if necessary.

Cementing. Special adhesives are used to bond pieces of foam together or to bond it to other materials, such as wood, metal, or plastics. Foam rubber *fabricating* cement is used for bonding rubber to rubber. It includes both the cement and the activator, which are mixed fresh for each job. *Pliobond* cement is used for bonding the rubber to other materials. To cement rubber, each surface is coated with the fabricating adhesive and allowed to get tacky; then it is pressed together and after a few minutes can be handled. Use the cement recommended by the manufacturer for the urethane foam.

Fig. 9–2. The foam rubber is removed from the mold.

Courtesy Goodyear Tire and Rubber Company

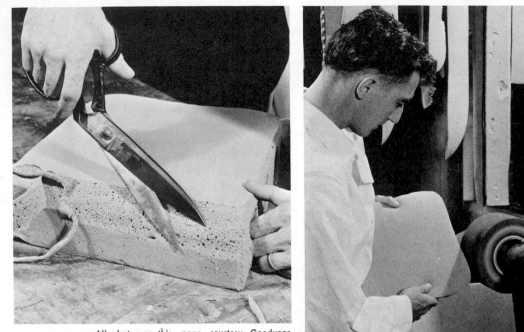

All photos on this page courtesy Goodyear
Tire and Rubber Company

Fig. 9—3 (above, left). The foam rubber stock is cut and trimmed with shears.
Fig. 9—4 (right). The trimmed surfaces of the cut foam rubber stock may be buffed
smooth to form the cushion. Fig. 9—5 (below). Various types of foam rubber for
upholstery. Note the cording in the thicker flat utility and molded stock.

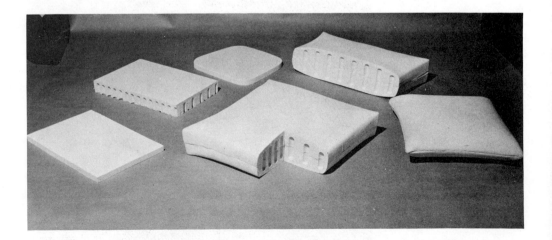

Edges and corners of the foam rubber need reenforcing because of the extra flexing they get. A fabric tape cemented to the foam does this.

SOLID BASES

Solid bases are very practical on chairs and couches. For dining chairs, at least 1″ foam is recommended in a firm or medium compression. For deep cushioning, use the heavier, cored stock.

In solid-base construction, ventilation should be provided to permit air to escape when the cushion is compressed. Forty-five to fifty ½″ holes in a plywood chair seat are adequate. Proportionally fewer are needed in backs and couch bases.

WEB BASES

Rubber upholstery webbing is commonly used to support foam seating. The webbing is stretched enough when installing to put it under light tension. The individual bands are spaced to suit. The more bands, the more support. A 2-inch spacing is generally adequate.

FABRIC COVERING

Any upholstery covering should fit snugly over the foam. To assure this, the foam is cut larger than the pattern. The amount will vary with the size, the thickness, and the compression of the cushion. Small pieces need about ¼″ extra on all sides; large pieces need as much as ¾″. The soft grades require more allowance than the firm.

The most difficult part of foam upholstery for the beginner is the fitting and sewing of the fabric. Corded edges are preferred because they hold their shape better. You will need the assistance of someone who is expert on the sewing machine for this.

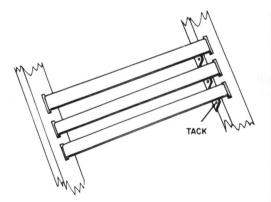

TACK

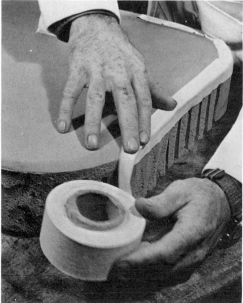

Fig. 9–7 Courtesy Goodyear Tire and Rubber Company

Fig. 9–6 (above). Rubber upholstery webbing. Fig. 9–7 (right). Tape is applied to foam rubber to reinforce edges and corners.

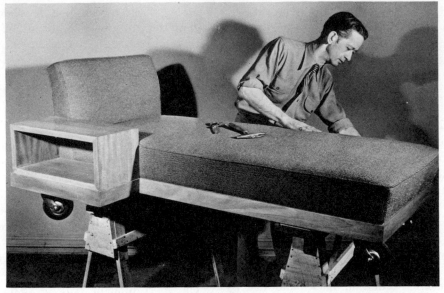

Fig. 9—8. A couch with a plywood bottom and foam rubber cushioning.

FOR RESEARCH, EXPERIMENT, DEVELOPMENT

1. Why is foam rubber springy?
2. Why are some grades more resilient than others?
3. Why has foam rubber become the modern cushioning?
4. Find the comparative qualities of rubber and plastic foam. (See *Resource Materials.*)

2

SECTION

RELATED WOOD SCIENCE AND TECHNOLOGY

WOOD SCIENCE AND TECHNOLOGY

Woodworking, like all of the subject-matter areas in industrial arts, involves applications of scientific facts and principles. To work intelligently with wood and to use wood products wisely requires an acquaintance with these applications.

The better one understands the characteristics of woods, the strengths and weaknesses of structures, the differences among finishes, the operation of woodworking machines, and the like, the more scientific he becomes and the more efficiently he works. Mastery of the "how" is facilitated by a knowledge of the "why."

The more one understands the roles of Nature and of the scientist in woods and woodworking, the more appreciative he becomes of man's accomplishments in this field, and the better qualified he is to pass judgment on achievements in wood. In the chart, "Typical Products of American Forests and of the American Technology," are listed a few of the products of trees. If one could count all of the products of American forests, he would probably have as many as four or five thousand. With research, new products are continually being developed.

The Forest Products Laboratory. The Forest Products Laboratory, a division of the Forest Service of the United States Department of Agriculture, is the major institution in this country devoted to scientific research and experiment with wood. It was established in 1910 at Madison, Wisconsin, and is maintained in cooperation with the University of Wisconsin. The Laboratory is engaged in a continuous searching for new and better ways to use woods. Its publications are many and may be obtained from the Superintendent of Documents, United States Government Printing Office, Washington, D. C.

TYPICAL PRODUCTS OF AMERICAN FORESTS AND OF
THE AMERICAN TECHNOLOGY

SAW LOGS	VENEERS	WOOD CHEMISTRY	MISCELLANEOUS
Construction Lumber for Buildings	**Package Veneers**	**Pulpwood in Paper Manufacture**	**Saw Dust**
Agricultural	Baskets		Artificial leather
Commercial	Boxes	Newsprint	Insulating brick
Industrial	Crates	Book	Insulation
Military	Hampers	Writing	Fireworks
Private	**Construction Plywood**	Printing	**Sap and Gum**
Public	Concrete forms	Wrapping	Maple sugar
Transportation	Pre-fab houses	Container board	Rosin
Industrial Lumber	Boats	Wall board	Balsam
Containers	Doors	**Paper Conversion**	Turpentine
Furniture	Cabinets	Abrasives	**Edible Fruits**
Machinery and equipment	Furniture	Boxes	Pecans
Vehicles	**Fancy Veneers**	Resin laminates	Walnuts
Musical instruments	Wall panel	Towels	Hickory nuts
Toys	Furniture	Wallpaper	Butternuts
Sports equipment	**Boat Plywood**	**By Products**	**Bark**
	Mine sweepers	Acids	Oil flavorings
	Sloops	Alcohol	Cascara
	Canoes	Acetone	Tannins
	Racing shells	Adhesives	Dyes
	Compregnated Plywood	Oils	**Roots**
	Airplane propellers	Fertilizers	Sassafras oil
	Bearings	Dyes	Tobacco pipes
	Gears	Plastics	**Hardboards**
	Table tops	Cellophane	Furniture
	Tubing	Photo film	Paneling
		Rayon	Signs
		Explosives	Toys
		Waste Wood	**Poles, Posts**
		Tannin	**Ties, Timbers**
		Wax	**Fuel**
		Oils	**Bolts**
		Tar	Ball bats
		Creosote	Tooth picks
		Formaldehyde	Wooden ware
			Barrel staves

Courtesy American Forest Products Industries, Inc.

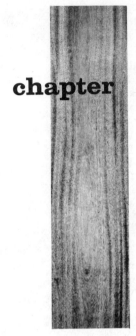

chapter **10**

ABOUT
TREES*

Trees are so common in most parts of the country that we seldom pause to wonder just what they actually are. If you ask a botanist or a forester he will tell you that a tree is a woody plant with one stem, or trunk, and a crown of leafy boughs. To be classified as a tree, a mature plant must be at least eight feet tall. Like any other plant it needs food, water, light, and warmth to grow.

The chemist sees it as a factory for manufacturing chemicals that he uses to create new materials, which in turn, are made into products for our living.

The engineer, the architect, and the builder see the tree as the source of

* Prepared with the assistance of the American Forest Products Industries, Inc.

buildings, bridges, and boats, and the woodworker sees it as beautiful furniture to make living more enjoyable.

WHY TREES ARE IMPORTANT

Ever since primitive man found that he could use a branch of a tree to protect himself and that he could tie a stick to a rock to make a hammer, trees have been important to people. Besides providing the American pioneer with fuel, nuts, berries, dyes, and medicines, trees gave him lumber for his houses, bridges, and vehicles. Today there are so many uses for wood that trees have become the raw material for huge industries employing millions of people. The wood-using industry is fourth among our industries in the value of its products and fourth in the number of people employed. Before they are harvested, trees perform other vital functions. They replenish the oxygen in the air we breathe. Have you noticed how much fresher country air seems than city air? Trees slow down damaging winds; they provide food and homes for birds, which help to keep down the insect population. Because most of our food comes from the soil, it is necessary that we take good care of it. Trees and grasses are our best means for protecting the soil. Trees prevent the destruction of the soil by helping to control erosion and by regulating the run-off of water. In addition to all of this, trees add a beauty, the scenic value of which can hardly be measured. With their interesting shapes and assortments of color, they grace the countryside and the city, adding enjoyment to our living.

ENEMIES OF TREES

Trees have many enemies that do tremendous damage. Fire is one of the worst. Each year there are about 100,000 forest fires which destroy some 12 million acres of timber. Because most of them are caused by careless people, it might be said that people are among the forests' worst enemies. Fire not only destroys or damages the trees, but the seeds and seedlings, too. It kills animals and birds and lays the land open to erosion. The use of radio, telephone, and airplanes and modern fire-fighting equipment make fire control easier today, but they do not eliminate the cause of fire.

The surest way to control fire is to see that it does not start. Small fires for burning trash or brush should be built only where there is no danger of the fire spreading. They should always be extinguished with water or dirt. If no water or loose dirt or sand is available, a fire should not be built. Careless smokers are a hazard anywhere, and especially in the forests. Perhaps your class could draw up a list of safety suggestions for smokers. Most important, we must impress upon everyone the dangers of forest fires, because nearly one-third of all forest fires are deliberately set for misguided or malicious reasons.

Fig. 10—1. A forest fire probably caused by a careless person.

Courtesy American Forest Products Industries, Incorporated

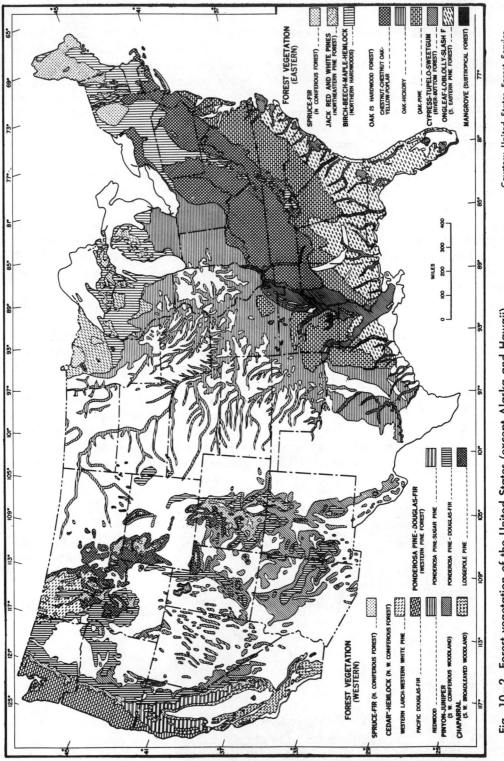

Fig. 10—2. Forest vegetation of the United States (except Alaska and Hawaii).

Courtesy United States Forest Service

FOREST VEGETATION
(EASTERN)

SPRUCE-FIR ————————
(N CONIFEROUS FOREST)

JACK RED AND WHITE PINES ————
(NORTHEASTERN PINE FOREST)

BIRCH-BEECH-MAPLE-HEMLOCK ————
(NORTHERN HARDWOODS)

OAK (S HARDWOOD FOREST) ————

CHESTNUT-CHESTNUT OAK-
YELLOW-POPLAR ————————

OAK-HICKORY ————————

OAK-PINE ————————

CYPRESS-TUPELO-SWEETGUM ————
(RIVER-BOTTOM FOREST)

LONGLEAF-LOBLOLLY-SLASH F ————
(S. EASTERN PINE FOREST)

MANGROVE (SUBTROPICAL FOREST) ————

FOREST VEGETATION
(WESTERN)

SPRUCE-FIR (N. CONIFEROUS FOREST) ————

CEDAR-HEMLOCK (N. W. CONIFEROUS FOREST) ————

WESTERN LARCH-WESTERN WHITE PINE ————

PACIFIC DOUGLAS-FIR ————

REDWOOD ————————

PINYON-JUNIPER ————
(S. W. CONIFEROUS WOODLAND)

CHAPARRAL ————
(S. W. BROADLEAVED WOODLAND)

PONDEROSA PINE-DOUGLAS-FIR ————
(WESTERN PINE FOREST)

PONDEROSA PINE-SUGAR PINE ————

PONDEROSA PINE-DOUGLAS-FIR ————

LODGEPOLE PINE ————

MILES
0   100   200   300   400

Insects destroy about four times as much timber as does fire. Certain beetles and moths attack and feed on the full-grown trees and actually kill thousands of acres of them each year. DDT sprayed by airplane and helicopter is effective against many leaf-eating insects.

Trees get diseases, too, especially after they are full grown. Dutch elm disease is killing off the elm so rapidly that unless control measures are taken at once, this most beautiful of American shade trees may become extinct. The chestnut, once a common tree, has become almost extinct because of a blight. For most tree diseases, the only cure is to remove the tree or the host plant from the forest before it infects others. Prompt harvesting of infected trees is also the best known way to halt bark beetles. Together insects and disease do nine times the annual damage done by fire.

CONSERVATION OF FORESTS

Conservation of forests means managing forests so that crop after crop of trees is produced on the same land. In addition to controlling forest enemies, it means leaving seed trees at harvest time so that Nature can reseed the cutover areas.

Many private woodlands have been certified by the American Tree Farm System. To win this blue-ribbon badge of good forestry, which is sponsored by the forest industries, the owner must provide adequate protection against fire, in-

Fig. 10—3 (below, left). Forest rangers stationed in towers such as this keep a constant watch for fires. Fig. 10—4 (below, right). Plowing a fire lane helps to prevent the spread of a fire.

Courtesy American Forest Products Industries, Incorporated

sects, disease, and excessive grazing, and use cutting practices that insure future crops of trees. There are about 16,700 certified Tree Farmers in the United States. Together they own nearly 50,-000,000 acres of forestland. They are proving to their friends and neighbors that good management makes tree growing profitable besides providing all the other forest benefits.

The forests of the United States are growing more timber than is being removed each year. This favorable balance in our forest "bank account" has been brought about largely by the use of better forest practices by lumber and paper companies, farmers, and other owners of private woodlands. Government forest lands have nearly always been well managed. The challenge before woodland owners now is to continue to increase the productiveness of their forests so as to provide the wood products that will be needed in the future by our growing

Courtesy American Forest Products Industries, Incorporated

Fig. 10—6. This sign identifies a tree farm.

population. It is especially important that farmers and other owners of small woodlots learn to practice forestry, because they own around half of the nation's forest acreage. Many industrial foresters work with them, teaching them how to take good care of their trees and produce more wood products.

GOVERNMENT AND THE FORESTS

The Federal government not only maintains the national parks and forests, but also furnishes expert assistance to private timber owners and lumber companies on forest management. The United States Forest Service carries on this program in conjunction with state forestry departments.

State-employed foresters work with county agricultural agents in most states at present. They distribute information

Fig. 10—5.   Fire fighting with back pumps.

Courtesy American Forest Products Industries, Incorporated

Courtesy American Forest Products Industries, Incorporated

Fig. 10—7 (left). Spraying DDT to destroy the tree-killing spruce bedworm. Fig. 10—8. In the Pacific Northwest, forest industries speed up getting harvested areas back into new timber crops or to give nature a hand in greening up old burns. Here a helicopter seeds timberlands in Oregon.

on forestry, conduct demonstrations on tree planting, insect control, and so forth for farmers and owners of small wood lots. With the cooperation of the county agents, they assist farmers with good woodlot management practices.

State universities promote 4-H clubs with the assistance of the county extension services. Many boys and girls choose forestry and conservation as their club projects.

The United States Soil Conservation Service is also concerned with trees. It helps farmers plan the use of their land to best conserve the soil. Tree farming and the establishment of small wood lots are encouraged. Trees must be important or so many different agencies and experts would not give attention to them.

HOW TO PLANT A TREE

There is a thrill in planting a tree and watching it grow through the years. The older you get, the more beautiful the tree becomes and the prouder you are that you planted it. You can start with a seed or seedling. Plant a seed in moist soil in a flower pot, and after a few weeks or months, depending on the kind of seed, a sprout pokes its way up and into the light. The soil should be kept moist, but not wet. You can plant such seeds as black walnuts, acorns, the pine seeds that fall from ripe pine cones, and many others. The tiny plants are called seedlings and should be planted out of doors in the spring or fall. Put them where they won't get trampled on and where they will be slightly shaded from the sun for the first year. After this first year they may be transplanted to a permanent location where stakes or wire fencing may be needed for protection.

4-H Club boys and girls plant many thousands of seedlings each year. They get them from nurseries. Here is a method they use for planting them.

1. The roots must be kept moist before, during, and after planting. Mix some soil and water in a pail to a mud and place the plants in it.

2. Press a spade 6 to 8 inches into the earth and lean forward on the handle to open a hole.
3. Place a seedling in the hole, spreading out its muddy roots.
4. Remove the shovel and step the soil firmly into place.

When seedlings die, it is usually because they don't get enough moisture. If you are planting only a few, it may be advisable to water them at planting and frequently thereafter unless rain is plentiful.

You can find out more about tree planting from your county agricultural agent. Be sure you get to plant at least one tree before you leave school. In his poem, "Trees," Joyce Kilmer wrote that "Only God can make a tree." We know this is true, but we can be of help to Him in His work by planting trees and by taking care of them.

Fig. 10—9. Marene replants her Christmas tree.

TREE SURGERY

Tree surgery is a field of work specializing in the care of shade or ornamental trees. It is interesting to watch a tree surgeon at work. He sprays trees for insects and diseases; he repairs injuries; he prunes unwanted branches; and he removes dead limbs. When a tree cannot be saved, he removes it and may plant a nearly full-grown one in its place.

Fig. 10—10 (left). Planting trees by machine. The man following the machine drops seedlings into a furrow opened by a plow. Then a packing wheel firms the soil around the seedling. Fig. 10—11 (right). A seedling nursery.

Courtesy American Forest Products Industries, Incorporated

CHEMISTRY AND THE TREE

A tree is a chemical factory. Operating automatically, it converts the raw materials—water, sunlight, minerals, and carbon dioxide—into cellulose, sugars, starches, lignin, and oxygen in its own growth process. Through its billions of tiny root hairs, the tree draws water from the particles of soil, channels it through the root system, and draws it up through the sapwood, which is a network of tiny cellulose tubes. These tubes carry the mineral-bearing water out into the veins of the leaves where it is evaporated from the pores on the undersides.

The leaf is the busy part of this factory, and the work it does is called *photosynthesis*. In this process, the water (H_2O) is combined with carbon dioxide (CO_2) which the leaves take from the air. Energy is supplied by the sun in evaporating the water, thus causing the "pull" of more water through the roots. This is known as *transpiration*. The sun also acts upon the *chlorophyll* (the green

Fig. 10—12. Wood is made of long narrow tubes, or cells, shown here magnified 50 times.

Courtesy United States Forest Service, Forest Products Laboratory

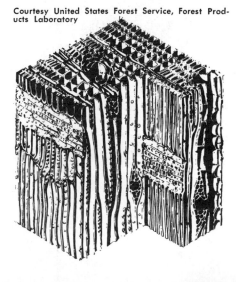

matter in the leaves), and the molecules of water and carbon dioxide are broken up. Then the atoms of carbon, hydrogen, and oxygen are rearranged into other chemicals which supply the tree with food. This food is in the form of starches and sugars. They are further processed in the cambium layer, the growth layer, and become cellulose, lignin, and other chemicals which go to make up wood, sap, oil, and gum. No man-made factory is so automatic or as efficient as is the growth process of the tree.

HOW A TREE GROWS

A tree grows outward from the center by adding new cells, or fibers, around itself—including trunk, branches, and roots—in a layer just beneath the bark. It also adds new fibers at the tips of the branches and roots. The limbs of trees grow longer and thicker, but the junction at the trunk remains at approximately the same height above ground. In the growth layer, the outward cells form the bark, and those inside form the wood. The sapwood is made of living, functioning cells, and the heartwood is made of the inactive cells that have formed the strong wood at the center of the tree. A season's growth is identified as an *annual ring*, and the inside part of this is called the *springwood* because of its rapid growth early in the season. The remainder is the *summerwood*, slower growing and denser.

KINDS OF TREES

There are more than 1,000 different kinds of trees in our forests, but only about 100 of them supply the nation's wood needs. The rest have little if any commercial value. Of this 100, about 40

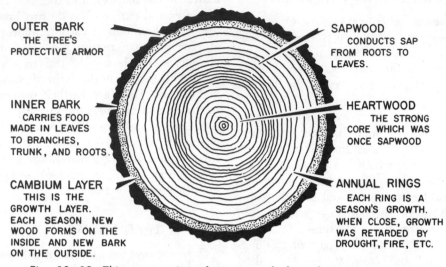

OUTER BARK
THE TREE'S
PROTECTIVE ARMOR

SAPWOOD
CONDUCTS SAP
FROM ROOTS TO
LEAVES.

INNER BARK
CARRIES FOOD
MADE IN LEAVES
TO BRANCHES,
TRUNK, AND ROOTS.

HEARTWOOD
THE STRONG
CORE WHICH WAS
ONCE SAPWOOD

CAMBIUM LAYER
THIS IS THE
GROWTH LAYER.
EACH SEASON NEW
WOOD FORMS ON THE
INSIDE AND NEW BARK
ON THE OUTSIDE.

ANNUAL RINGS
EACH RING IS A
SEASON'S GROWTH.
WHEN CLOSE, GROWTH
WAS RETARDED BY
DROUGHT, FIRE, ETC.

Fig. 10—13. This cross-section of a tree trunk shows how a tree grows.

are known as *softwoods* and the rest as *hardwoods*. The softwood trees are chiefly the "evergreens," which hold their leaves the year around. More correctly, they are the *conifers* and include pines, spruces, firs, hemlocks, balsams, and so forth.

The hardwoods have broad leaves which are usually shed in the autumn. These are called *deciduous*. Common varieties include oak, ash, hickory, walnut, maple, cherry, basswood, and birch.

The oldest living things are trees. There is a cypress that is estimated by experts to be 4,000 years old standing near Oaxaco, Mexico. Its circumference is so great that 24 men with arms outstretched can barely circle it.

FOR RESEARCH, EXPERIMENT, DEVELOPMENT

1. What contributions do trees make to our living?
2. How are forest fires started?
3. How should a Christmas tree be transplanted?
4. How can one make a shade house for seedlings?
5. How does a tree produce oxygen?
6. What causes the grain in wood?
7. Why does sanding across the grain scratch wood and sanding with the grain does not?
8. What methods are used for fighting forest fires?
9. What makes the color in wood?
10. Can the color of the wood in a tree be changed? How?

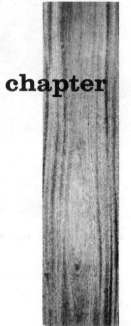

chapter 11

ABOUT
WOOD*

Although woods from different trees have decidedly different qualities, all woods are essentially the same physically and chemically. All wood is made up of cells which, because they are long and slender, are called fibers. These fibers are about ¼″ long and ¹⁄₁₀₀₀″ in diameter, or about the size of a whisker. A nonfibrous material, lignin, holds the fibers together and makes the wood tough and flexible. The cell cavities in seasoned wood are dead air spaces that make the wood light in weight and effective as heat and sound insulation. Woods with very small cell cavities (e.g., lignum vitae) are hard, and difficult to work.

* Based on publications of the Forest Products Laboratory.

CHEMICAL NATURE OF WOOD

The solid part of wood is chiefly cellulose, which is composed of carbon, hydrogen, and oxygen. About 60 per cent of wood is cellulose, and about 28 per cent is lignin which, although made up of the same elements, is entirely different in its properties. In addition, other substances, such as minerals, starches, sugars, resins, dyes, oils, and gums, are found in wood. Altogether, wood is approximately 50 per cent carbon, 6 per cent hydrogen, and 44 per cent oxygen.

PORES

Pores are tubes made up of large cells placed end-to-end vertically through the

Fig. 11—1 (left). Wood chips are cooked with chemicals to produce refined cellulose. Fig. 11—2 (above). The pulp is further refined in a beater.

wood. They conduct sap from the roots to the leaves. Coarse-textured woods such as oak, ash, and balsa are called *open-porous*, because the cavities can be clearly seen on the surface of the wood. The fine-textured woods such as maple and cherry are *close-porous*, because the cavities can be seen only with a magnifier.

MEDULLARY, OR WOOD RAYS

Wood rays are rows of cells that in some woods can be seen running across the end grain from the center of the log to the edge, like spokes in a wheel. They serve to transfer foodstuffs horizontally in the tree from bark to pith and to store foodstuff. In a piece of oak you will find the rays clearly defined; in pines they can be seen only with a magnifier.

ANNUAL RINGS

Annual rings are made up of cells. Those which are produced in the spring growth of the tree, next to the bark, are generally much larger than those produced late in the season. In the same area a fairly abrupt transition is visible between the two growths. Together they make up the annual ring. Normally the rings can be counted in a log to determine the age of a tree (see Fig. 10-13). The early growth is called *springwood*; the late, *summerwood*.

HEARTWOOD AND SAPWOOD

In the growth of a tree, new cells are produced under the cambium layer, as *sapwood*. This gradually changes into *heartwood*, which becomes the wood characteristic of the tree. It is usually darker in color than the sapwood.

WOOD GRAIN

The differences in cell structure produce a distinct pattern within the wood itself. This becomes characteristic for each kind, but never identical in any two pieces of the same wood. Distortion of the fibers due to misshapen growth, limbs, burls, and such affects the grain figure. The way a log is sawed also affects the figure. Those woods that have considerable difference between springwood and summerwood are called *coarse-grained*; when there is little contrast, they are called *fine-grained*.

Straight-grained wood has its fibers running in the same direction as the main axis of the tree.

Interlocked grain occurs when layers of the wood alternate in direction. Such wood is difficult to split and to plane; for example, red gum, mahogany, elm, and cottonwood.

Wavy grain is a nearly regular pattern of ripples or waves in the grain.

Curly grain is a grain pattern having a definite curly appearance similar to "bird's-eye" maple.

Burls are growths that develop as the tree heals over branch stubs or groups of buds. The wood is highly figured and valuable. It is common in maple, walnut, and black cherry.

Knots are sections through limbs. The grain pattern about them is circular and is generally more varied in direction than wood above or below the knot.

HOW LUMBER IS SAWED

There are two basic methods for sawing lumber from logs. When boards are

PLAIN-SAWED LUMBER

QUARTER-SAWED LUMBER
THIS IS THE ORIGINAL METHOD. THERE ARE MANY VARIATIONS.

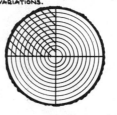

Fig. 11—3. Lumber is either plain-sawed or quarter-sawed from logs.

sawed off with cuts made at right angles to the rays, and tangent to the rings, they are *plain-sawed*. When the cuts are made from the bark to the center of the log, the lumber is *quarter-sawed*. Plain-sawed lumber is cheaper to cut and has less waste. It dries more rapidly and in some woods produces the most beautiful grain pattern. Quarter-sawed lumber holds its shape better, wears more evenly (as in flooring), and in some woods produces the greatest beauty.

SPECIFIC GRAVITY OF WOOD

The specific gravity of wood is the ratio of the weight of a volume of wood to an equal volume of pure water at 4 degrees C. Because water weighs approximately 62.5 pounds per cubic foot, a wood that has a specific gravity of 0.38 will weigh 23.75 pounds per cubic foot (62.5 × 0.38). Specific gravity is one of the qualities with which wood chemists and engineers are concerned in their work with wood. Specific gravities of the more common woods are: basswood, black willow, butternut, 0.30-0.36; white pine, yellow poplar, Douglas fir, 0.36-0.42; black cherry, elm, ash, 0.42-0.50; black walnut, oak, sugar maple, 0.50-0.60; and pecan, dogwood, hickory, 0.60-0.72.

Wood is not a homogeneous matter, however. Its cellular structure is such that a board may have different densities from end to end and from edge to edge. This causes problems in drying and shrinking, but makes wood a unique material with which to work.

MOISTURE

The sapwood of green trees may contain more than 100 per cent of moisture by weight. The heartwood usually has less, sometimes as low as 30 per cent. After lumber is air dried, the amount of moisture left varies with the size of the pieces, the atmosphere, the length of the period of seasoning, and the density of the wood. Wood dried in moist regions contains about 12-15 per cent moisture, but it may run to 30 per cent. Air drying is a slow process, either as a method of conditioning some woods for use or as a preliminary to kiln drying. All woods tend to reach a state of moisture balance or "equilibrium moisture content" with the surrounding atmospheric humidity.

Moisture appears in two forms in lumber: free water and hygroscopic water. Free water is held within the cell cavities. Hygroscopic water is that contained within the cell walls. It is this latter type of water which returns to kiln dried wood from the atmosphere. It even penetrates paint and varnish.

Properly kiln dried lumber will have less moisture than air dried, perhaps as low as 4 to 6 per cent. To retain the advantages of such low moisture contents, kiln dried lumber must be given proper care; the kiln dried state does not guarantee it against a later absorption of excessive moisture. Kiln dried stock is preferred for furniture. Wood used too wet, either kiln or air dried, may give trouble with warping, checking and cracking of glue joints.

SHRINKING AND SWELLING

One of the undesirable qualities of wood is its tendency to shrink and swell. Shrinking results when water leaves the cell walls, and swelling, when it is absorbed. A piece of wood does not shrink uniformly in all directions; it shrinks least in length and most in width when the board is cut tangentially with the rings. Finishes applied to wood reduce the rate at which it absorbs moisture.

KILN DRYING

Kiln drying is the most effective means for seasoning lumber to be used in manufacturing. The kiln is a large insulated chamber in which lumber is exposed to circulating heated air. Here the green lumber gives up its free water and most of the hygroscopic. Different kinds of woods require somewhat different heat treatment, but the maximum temperatures generally used are in the range of 120-130 degrees F. Each wood has its critical temperature beyond which it must not be heated. Excess heating causes a breakdown in the cell structure.

During kiln drying, wood begins to shrink when the free water has been removed and the fibers begin to give up

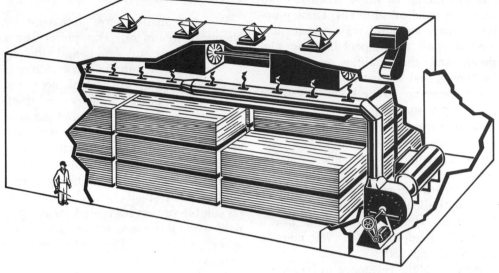

Fig. 11—4. The interior of an industrial dry kiln. Note the heating and ventillating system.

their hygroscopic water. Too rapid drying causes an uneven shrinkage and a checking of the surface of the board. The surface dries first and tries to contract, but the moist inner wood prevents it. Consequently, the surface checks, producing a network of fine cracks.

Plain sawed lumber dries more quickly than quarter sawed. Sapwood dries faster than heartwood. Moisture leaves the end grain faster than the surface grain. These differences cause strains within the board which results in warping, cupping, winding, splitting, and other defects.

COLOR AND WOOD

Woods vary in color, from the black of ebony to the white of holly, through dark browns, red browns, light browns, yellows, and greens. Sapwood is usually lighter in color than heartwood. Some woods contain so much coloring material that it can be extracted for dyes; for example, yellows from osage orange, browns from walnut, and reds from dogwood roots.

Most lumber darkens when exposed to light and air. Try this with a piece of white pine taken from the bottom of the stack. Lay it on the window sill with part of it covered; after a few days notice the difference. Philippine mahogany bleaches in light. Heat also darkens the color of lumber, as does submersion in water. The fumed oak finish is a dark brown color obtained by exposing oak to ammonia fumes. The ammonia reacts with the lignin.

STRENGTHS OF WOOD

The mechanical qualities of wood are those qualities by which it resists changes in size or shape when it is affected by mechanical forces. These properties are: strengths of compression, tension, static and impact bending, and shear; and the qualities of stiffness, toughness, and hardness.

Compression strength is given in pounds per square inch as the average maximum resistance to crushing, parallel to the grain. Air dried walnut has a compressive strength of approximately 10,000 pounds, while basswood has only 2,200.

The tensile strength is the resistance to being pulled apart in the direction of the grain. Here black walnut has a strength of approximately 780 pounds, and basswood, 280.

Bending is the resistance to forces applied as a load on a horizontal beam. *Shear* is resistance to an action of parallel but opposing forces, similar to that of a pair of shears cutting paper. *Stiffness* is the resistance to bending, and *toughness* is the ability to resist shock. *Hardness* is the resistance to denting.

PRESERVING WOOD

Wood is made more permanent by chemical treatment. The preservatives are poisonous to fungi and insects. Creosote, an oil soluble preservative, is used on railroad ties, telephone poles, fence posts, bridge timbers, and such items, where the dark color and the odor are not objectionable. Chromated zinc chloride and a number of other water soluble preservatives are also used as well as considerable quantities of pentachlorophenol (penta), a relatively clear oil soluble preservative used for treating new window frames, sashes, doors, and other parts of buildings. Penta may be painted over.

WOOD IDENTIFICATION

The identity of wood begins with the tree. Different species have different characteristics. The tree profile, the nature of the leaves, including color, shape,

Fig. 11—5. A scientist in his laboratory cuts wood samples to study.

Courtesy Western Pine Association

and veining, the color and texture of the bark, the positioning of the branches, all aid in identification.

When sawed into lumber, woods from different species of trees have unique qualities. Among these are color, fragrance, grain pattern, and density.

Cell structure and arrangement as seen under a microscope also vary with the species. For example, make a clean cut with a razor blade across a small section of the end grain of several different kinds of wood. Note the cell sizes and locations with a magnifier. Some will have the cells arranged in a ring concentric with the annual rings. These are called *ring porous*. Others have the cells spread throughout the growth. These are called *diffuse porous*.

Wood identification, you see, becomes rather scientific. To study this further, see the references at the end of the book.

FOR RESEARCH, EXPERIMENT, DEVELOPMENT

1. What chemicals are obtained from trees?
2. How does a tree grow?
3. What is the moisture content of wood in your school's lumber rack?
4. How do differences in grain pattern result with differences in cuts?
5. Why is wood stronger across the grain than in the direction of the grain?
6. Why will a true, flat board sometimes warp or wind when ripped down the middle?
7. How can you measure the density of a wood?
8. Why does wood absorb water faster through the end grain than through the face?
9. Identify several different woods.
10. What kinds of wood were used for the construction of World War I aircraft?

chapter 12

ABOUT
WOOD
ADHESIVES*

The development of adhesives for bonding wood together has been the subject of considerable research during the past twenty years. Even the terms, "cement," "glue," and "adhesive" have been redefined for purposes of clarifying meanings. The American Society for Testing Materials uses the term *cement* to include adhesives compounded from rubber, using organic solvents. *Glue* is considered to be a slang term applied generally to adhesives for wood. It has been popularly used to include all types of adhesives, especially those that are "sticky." *Adhesives* is considered the

* This section was prepared with the assistance of The Divisions of Research & Development, of the United States Plywood Corporation and of the Franklin Glue Company.

most scientifically acceptable term for wood bonding agents.

THEORIES OF ADHESION

Until about 1942 it was believed that adhesives held wood together by a kind of mechanical fastening. Wood being porous, the adhesive penetrated the cells with "stalagmite-like tentacles" and, when set, was firmly attached. This is the mechanical theory of bonding and today is considered to have but a minor part in the bonding of woods. Good glues in this case have a natural stickiness about them.

The currently acceptable explanation is given in the *specific adhesion* theory. Certain materials capable of forming strong films have a great affinity for wood. It is believed that in some cases chemical reaction between the adhesive and the wood aids the specific adhesion. It is known, for example, that in phenol formaldehyde resin bonds, the adhesive reacts with the wood cellulose to form other products.

NATURAL AND SYNTHETIC ADHESIVES

Natural adhesives from such sources as animals, fish, casein, and soya beans are known to adhere by specific adhesion. Both wood and these adhesives are *hydrophilic* in that they absorb water in wetting and give it up in drying, and are consequently attracted to each other rather than repelled.

Natural glues are being replaced with synthetic glues, because of the latter's superior characteristics, which are easier to produce and to control. The only waterproof adhesives are synthetic, but not all synthetics are waterproof. For interior use waterproof adhesives are generally not necessary. Synthetic adhesives are known as resins and include phenol formaldehyde, urea formaldehyde, melamine formaldehyde, and melamine-urea formaldehyde—chemical names for certain well-known plastics.

HOW ADHESIVES SET

The setting of adhesives varies with the type. In all cases the first stage is the wetting of the wood surfaces. This is why they are liquid. In the second stage the solvent in the agent is lost. This may be water, alcohol, or some other solvent. The third stage, curing, in synthetics involves the completion of the chemical action, and sometimes is facilitated by heat, a catalyst, or electronic waves.

GLUING PRESSURES

For maximum joint strength, there must be maximum contact of the glued surfaces. Clamping is used to keep the surfaces in contact until the setting of the adhesive takes over. The clamping also assures a minimum of glue film between the surfaces. Greater strength results from a thin film than from a thick. The pressures used in clamping are generally in the range of 100-150 p.s.i. (pounds per square inch). While you may not be able to measure it each time you tighten a clamp, this pressure should not be so great as to damage the wood or bend the clamp.

ELECTRONIC GLUING

The use of high frequency electronic waves speeds up the setting of the adhesive and makes the setting uniform throughout the assembly. This is commonly used in laminating bench tops and in veneering. The adhesive is powdered resin, technically known as powdered urea formaldehyde. This is a thermosetting resin, which means that it cures with heat. Some of the heat is produced in the chemical action within the mixture itself. The electronic system provides additional heating.

TESTING ADHESIVES

Manufacturers refer to the American Society of Testing Materials for standards on testing adhesives. In general, if the bond is stronger than the wood, that is as strong as it needs to be. Boiling and soaking in water over prolonged periods are used to test water-resistance. Various mechanical tests are used to determine the holding power.

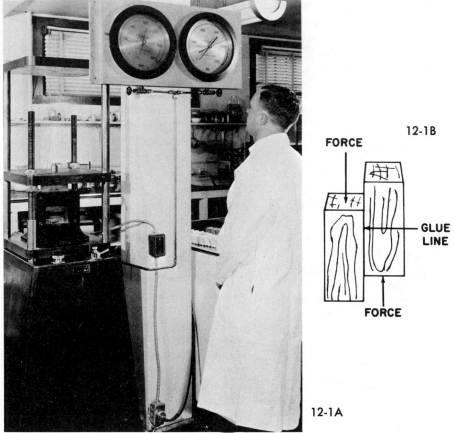

12-1B

FORCE

GLUE
LINE

FORCE

12-1A

Courtesy The Franklin Glue Company

Fig. 12-1A (left). Compression block shear testing apparatus. Fig. 12-1B (right). Block shear test showing direction of forces.

The compression block shear test is the most commonly used for testing wood adhesives in high stress applications, such as laminating, assembly, and edge jointing. Hard maple blocks are glued together as perfectly as possible. The compressive force is applied slowly until the joint gives way. The amount of the breaking force is read on a dial (see Figs. 12-1A and 12-1B). This force may run as high as 3,000-4,000 p.s.i for high quality glue.

The NAFM (National Association of Furniture Manufacturers) test is used with cross lap glued blocks. It measures the tension required to rupture the joint (see Figs. 12-2A and 12-2B).

The impact test records the number of footpounds required to break the joint. This test is for glues used on bowling pins, chairs, and other such articles which are usually subjected to impact rather than to static loads (see Figs. 12-3A and 12-3B).

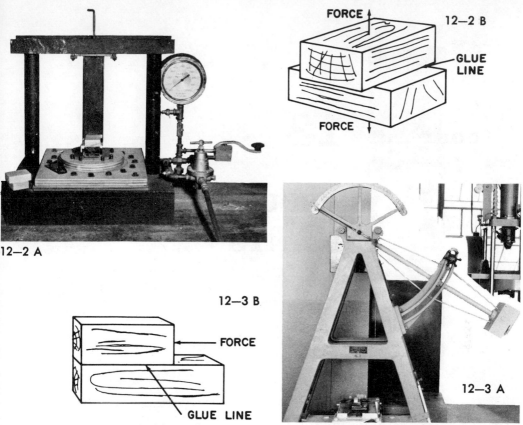

Apparatus to test holding power of adhesives. Line drawing shows direction of forces. Fig. 12—2 A and B. The NAFM test for cross lap joints. Fig. 12—3 A and B. The ASTM impact test.

FOR RESEARCH, EXPERIMENT, DEVELOPMENT

1. Devise equipment for testing adhesive strengths. A hydraulic press with a pressure gauge such as found in a garage or machine shop can be used.
2. Compare the strengths of different types of adhesives, natural vs. synthetic.
3. Compare adhesive strengths on green and kiln dried wood.
4. Test hardened adhesives for solubility in finishing solvents: paint thinner, lacquer thinner, etc.
5. How could the comparative holding power of adhesives and wood screws be determined experimentally?
6. Why does a glue not have to be "sticky"?
7. Why is end grain gluing not as strong as edge grain?
8. Develop a clamping system to hold the staves in the shell of a bongo drum.

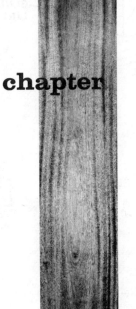

chapter **13**

ABOUT
PAINTS*

The term *paints* includes all of those materials, both natural and synthetic, commonly known as paint, varnish, enamel, lacquer, and the like, which are used as surface coatings on other materials. They serve two main purposes: protection and decoration. Paints can provide wood with considerable protection from moisture, weathering, strong chemicals, soiling, wear, fire, and insect and fungus damage. Clear finishes can emphasize the beauty of wood, while opaque finishes can conceal it.

COMPOSITION OF PAINTS

In actual usage the term paint generally refers to pigment-bearing coatings. As such, paint is a mixture of solids and

* This section was prepared with the assistance of the Sherwin-Williams Company.

liquids. The solids are called *pigments*; they provide color and opacity as well as protection. The liquid is composed of gums and drying oils, and is called the *vehicle*, because it carries the solids in suspension and to the surface being coated.

Pigments are usually metals or minerals. For white, titanium, zinc, and lead are used. Prussian blue is made from iron; chrome yellow, from lead; and black, from carbon.

The gums and oils make the paint more durable, easier to apply, resistant to acids and alkalis, and help to bind the particles of pigment together. Among the natural oils used are linseed, tung, castor, and soya bean. Gums are originally natural rosins from trees; synthetic gums are known as resins.

The solvent, or thinner, is added to make the mixture more fluid. It must be one that is compatible with the rest of the ingredients. This is why no one solvent can be used for all paints.

PAINT MANUFACTURING

A few decades ago paints were made by painters. A house painter, for example, had his own recipe. He bought the oils, pigments, and solvents, all of which were the natural forms, and mixed them for each job. Today paint is industrially manufactured to chemists' formulas and is closely related to plastics and rubber manufacturing. Surface coatings are made from nearly all of the major types of plastics manufactured.

Once the formula has been developed, the paint goes into production. Pigments, gums and oils are mixed in huge grinding mills, or ball mills, where each tiny particle of pigment is coated and dispersed. The result is a paste to which other oils, solvents, and color concentrates are added. Machines fill containers with this paint and label them.

APPLICATION OF PAINTS

In addition to the familiar paint brush, roller, spray gun, and aerosol "paint package," there are several other methods of applying paints. The latter are used largely by industry. Dipping is a common process for coating articles. They are attached to conveyors which move them through tanks of paint and into dryers. Industrial spraying is often done automatically as the articles move along on conveyors.

Some recent developments in paint application include the *hot spray* method. Paint is heated to 120-150 degrees, which thins it for spraying. This heating takes the place of thinners. Advantages of this method are: a reduction in pin-holes in the coating; heavier coatings with each pass of the spray gun, thus saving time; greater opacity per coat; and it permits the spraying of heavy, viscous coating materials. The spraying can be done at lower room or outdoor temperatures than other types of spraying.

Hydraulic spraying involves the application of high pressures to the paint itself by pumping. When it is forced from the nozzle of the spray gun, the paint atomizes without the need for compressed air as is ordinarily required. This method is also combined with the hot spray process.

Spray guns with double nozzles are being used with synthetic coatings. The paint is sprayed from one nozzle at the same time as the *catalyst*, or drier, is sprayed from the other.

As new types of finishes are developed, new techniques of application are devised. The old trusty paint brush has had its day in industry, but still serves the home craftsman. It is estimated that as much as 65 per cent of all the paint sold in this country is applied by the do-it-yourself painter.

HOW PAINT DRIES

Different types of paint dry differently. Some such as shellac and lacquer, dry through the *evaporation* of the solvent. Others dry by *oxidation*, the combining of oxygen from the air with the oils in the paint. Heat is applied to some paints for drying. This causes the paint molecules to enlarge, thus making the paint film increasingly solid as it dries. The chemical process is called *polymerization*.

SHELLAC

Shellac is a natural gum produced as a secretion of the lac insect common to India. It is scraped from branches of trees, cleaned, melted, and hardened into *orange* shellac. This is bleached to make *white* shellac. Shellac is dissolved in denatured alcohol four pounds to one gallon for the standard cut.

VARNISH

Varnish is a transparent coating usually made with synthetic resins and drying oils. The mixture is heated until the resins melt and blend with the oils. The solvent and driers are added. Varnish dries by both evaporation and oxidation. There are several types of varnishes, each intended for different uses. Spar varnish is water-resistant. Varnish may be obtained as glossy, semi-glossy, or flat. *Enamels* are pigmented varnishes.

LACQUERS

Lacquer is a transparent synthetic coating made of nitrocellulose, resins, plasticizer, and solvent. The nitrocellulose makes a tough, hard body, and the resins add gloss and adhesive qualities. The plasticizer makes the coating flexible, as is needed on the fabric covering of light airplanes, for example. Here the lacquer is called *dope*. The solvent dissolves all of the ingredients and thins it for application. When the lacquer is applied, the solvent dissolves the dry coats each time a new one is added, instead of building up in layers. Lacquer is characteristically quick drying; some types dry in five minutes or even less. It is the original plastics-type finish.

NEW TYPES OF PAINTS

The paint chemist has introduced several new types of paints since World War II. The synthetic *latex* paints for interior decoration include rubber-base paints. Although not made from rubber, they are made from some of the same raw materials from which synthetic rubber is made. Such paints, using a water solvent, are *emulsions.*

Alkyd paints are those synthetics made from alkyd resins, in turn chemically derived from alcohols and acids. These paints are durable, washable, and odorless. Mineral solvents are used.

In addition to these now common types there are many others, including phenolic and vinyl resins, polyvinal acetates, and acrylates, to name but a few. Paint making today is applied chemistry. New types continue to appear, so the woodworker must be alert for new products.

FOR RESEARCH, EXPERIMENT, DEVELOPMENT

1. What materials are commonly used for pigments in paints?
2. What vehicles are used in lacquers, synthetic enamels, and house paints?
3. Why is aluminum paint good protection for wood?
4. Why may a heavy coat of paint dry slowly, incompletely?
5. What solvent is used for an oil emulsion?

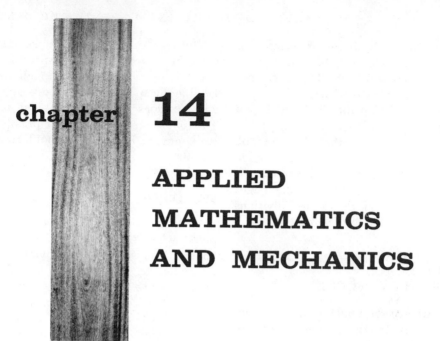

chapter 14

APPLIED MATHEMATICS AND MECHANICS

Mathematics is probably used just as much in working with wood as with other materials, even though a beginning craftsman cannot work as precisely with wood as he can, for example, with metal. Tolerances of ± ⅓₂″ are accurate in wood but not in machine metal work. Expert pattern makers can work with an accuracy in thousandths of an inch.

Board Measure. The unit of board measure is the *board foot*. This is a piece 1″ thick and 12″ square. With stock less than an inch thick, the board foot is used as a square foot. To find board feet, use this formula:

Thickness, in inches × width, in feet, × length, in feet = board feet.

Lumber is usually sold by the "M," which is 1,000 board feet.

Miters. When two angularly cut pieces fit together to make a joint, it is called a *miter*. The common miter forms a right angle, or 90 degrees. When made in two pieces, each is cut at 45 degrees. If the joint were 60 degrees, each would be cut at 30 degrees.

Roof Pitches. The slope of a roof is expressed as *pitch*. This is the ratio of the *rise* to the *span*. The span is the width of the building and the rise is the altitude of the triangle formed by the roof. When a roof has a rise of 20′ and a span of the same, the ratio is 20/20, or 1, and it is called a *full* pitch. For *half-pitch* the rise is one-half the altitude, or 10′; and for a *quarter-pitch*, it is 5′.

Degrees are sometimes used in expressing roof angles. With the use of elementary trigonometry the full pitch roof has an angle of 63 degrees. This is obtained by using the formula:

$$\text{Tan } A = \frac{a}{b}.$$

Substituting in this formula,

$$\text{Tan } A = \frac{20}{10}, \text{ or } 2.$$

In the Tangent Column of a table of trigonometric functions, the nearest number to 2.0000 is 1.9626. The angle opposite this number is 63 degrees.

Dividing a Board into Strips of Equal Width. This can be done without the use of arithmetic. Lay the rule across the board, with each end touching an edge of the board. The angle does not matter, so long as the rule touches the edges of the board. Make the desired divisions on the rule and mark them on the board.

BALANCE AND CENTRIFUGAL FORCE

The wood lathe tends to jump around when a large, rough piece of stock is being turned. This tendency is due to the existence of a state of unbalanced action. An accurately turned plate of large diameter will revolve at a high speed with very little vibration. Suppose the plate is 12″ in diameter and that a one-ounce weight is fastened to the rim at one point. Although the speed is the same, excessive vibration is noticed. The weight is being forced to move in a circular path when it would rather fly off at a tangent. If the speed is increased, the weight will eventually fly off. Note this calculation:

$$C = 0.00034 \times W \times R \times N^2,$$

where
 C is the centrifugal force
 W is the weight, in pounds
 R is the radius, in feet, between the center of the lathe spindle and the center of gravity of the weight,
 N is the revolutions per minute.

Taking the example of a 12″ plate, a one-ounce weight, and 1,500 rpm, this small weight exerts an unbalanced force of 24 pounds, which is enough to cause considerable lathe vibration.

This explanation suggests the importance of the control of the speed in the wood lathe when turning rough stock. Double the speed in the formula and see what it does to the centrifugal force. This is also true of the drill press. The work must be held so it can not turn with the bit.

SPEEDS OF MACHINES

Machine speeds can be easily computed when the speed of the motor is known. The speed of a driving pulley is related to the speed of the driven pulley as are the respective diameters. For example, when the jigsaw motor turns at 1,725 rpm with a 2″ pulley, and the saw pulley is 3″ in diameter, the latter turns at ⅔ of the motor speed, or approximately 1,150 rpm. No allowance is being made for motor load which reduces the speed.

The speed of a pair of gears is in the ratio of the respective numbers of teeth. While a pair of gears turn in opposite directions, a pair of pulleys turn in the same direction.

MEASURING MOISTURE CONTENT

The moisture content of wood is taken from a sample not less than 1″ in length, cut across the grain. This sample is cut not less than 24″ from an end of the board. It is weighed accurately in grams and placed in an oven at approximately 212 degrees F. When it no longer loses weight, it is oven-dry. The dry weight is subtracted from the original weight to find the amount of moisture lost. The weight lost is divided by the dry weight, and multiplied by 100, to find the per cent of moisture.

SOLVING RIGHT TRIANGLES

$A + B + C = 180°$

$C = A + B$

$A = 180° - (B + C)$

$B = 180° - (A + C)$

$c^2 = a^2 + b^2$

$c = \sqrt{a^2 + b^2}$

$a = \sqrt{c^2 - b^2}$

$b = \sqrt{c^2 - a^2}$

$\sin A = \dfrac{a}{c} = \cos B$

$\cos A = \dfrac{b}{c} = \sin B$

$\tan A = \dfrac{a}{b} = \cot B$

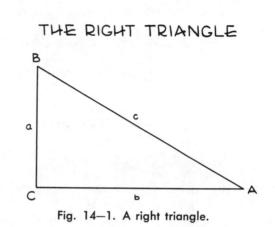

THE RIGHT TRIANGLE

Fig. 14—1. A right triangle.

MEASUREMENT AIDS

EQUIVALENTS

Length

1 foot = 12 inches
1 yard = 3 feet
1 rod = 16½ feet
1 mile = 5280 feet

Area

1 square foot = 144 square inches
1 square yard = 9 square feet

Volume

1 cubic foot = 1728 cubic inches

Volumes of Liquids

16 ounces = 1 pint
2 standard cups = 1 pint
3 teaspoons = 1 tablespoon
16 tablespoons = 1 cup

FORMULAS

Circles

Diameter = 2r (radius)
Circumference = πd (diameter)
(π = 3.1416 or 3½)
Area = πr²

Areas

Square = length × length
Rectangle = length × width
Triangle = $\dfrac{a \times b}{2}$ (See Fig. 14-1.)

Volumes

Cube and rectangular box =
              L × W × H
Cylinder = Area of base × height
1 cubic foot water weighs 62.5 lbs.

SOME PRACTICAL PROBLEMS

1. How is the rotary motion of the motor changed to a reciprocating motion in a jig saw?
2. How much will a 4′ × 8′ sheet of cardboard cost at 11¢ per square foot?
3. How much will 61″ × 10″ white pine boards 12′ long cost at $180.00 per M?
4. If a wood lathe has 4-step pulleys on motor and saw, of 2″, 3″, and 5″ diameters, what speeds does the head spindle have when the motor turns at 1,725 rpm?
5. If a gallon of enamel will cover 400 sq. ft., how much will a half-pint cover?
6. How long is the blade on a band saw which has 24″ diameter wheels whose centers are 36″ apart?
7. On the above saw, when the wheels are driven by a 2½″ motor pulley turning at 1,725 rpm., what is the speed of the blade in feet per minute?
8. What is the weight of a block of American black walnut 2″ × 4″ × 12″ when its specific gravity is 0.50?
9. What is the per cent of moisture in a sample of wood that has an oven-dry weight of 200 grams and weighs 275 grams before drying?
10. If you are to make a quart of shellac wash coat, using the proportion of 2 shellac to 1 alcohol, how many cups of each are required?

(Answers at end of chapter.)

NAIL HOLDING POWER

In general, the greater the specific gravity of a wood, the better it holds nails. However, this nail holding quality varies with the kind of wood, its thickness, and the direction of the grain. The size, number, and position of the nails have an effect also.

The end grain holds nails only about 50 per cent as well as the side grain. Dry wood holds them better than green; hardwoods, better than soft. When the nail is driven, the wood fibers are compressed. The greater the resistance to this compression, the more firmly the nail will be held in the wood.

The larger the diameter of the nail, the better it is held, up to the point of splitting the wood. To eliminate splitting, thin nails must be used, and they must be placed well in from the edge. The longer the nail, the better it holds. Slanting the nails also increases holding.

The Forest Products Laboratory recommends that for general nailing, the "d" or penny of the nail should not be greater than the thickness of the wood in eighths of an inch.

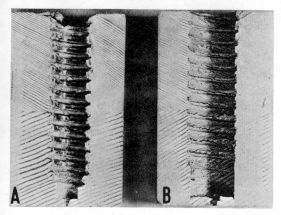

Fig. 14—2. A cut-away section through wood screw holes. A. Threads cut into wood by a correctly fitted screw. B. Shallow threads have little holding power. The pilot hole was bored too large.

SCREW HOLDING POWER

The holding power of a wood screw varies with the density of the wood and the grain direction, as well as with the length and diameter of the screw. *The resistance to withdrawal,* as the technicians call it, varies in the side grain of the wood as the square of the specific gravity of the wood. The holding power of the end grain is approximately 75 per cent that of the side grain. Consequently, to get the same holding in the end grain, one should use about one-fourth more screws, or screws about one-fourth longer. The denser the wood, the larger the pilot hole must be to prevent the screw from twisting off.

WOOD STRUCTURES

The joining of woods to produce the greatest strength with the least amount of wood and work is a goal of good de-

sign and involves some fundamental engineering. The major problems to be considered are:

1. The relatively high coefficient of expansion under the conditions of heat and moisture.
2. The weakness of joints when the end grain is glued.
3. The relationship of close fit in joints to strength.
4. The relationship of wood strength to direction of the grain.
5. The relationship of glue area in a joint to strength.

The tendency of wood to contract and expand with changes in temperature and moisture can be controlled somewhat by kiln drying. The sealing qualities of surface coatings provides some control. The tendency is neutralized in plywoods by the alternating of the grain. In some constructions, provision must be made for the actual movement of the wood during

Fig. 14—3. A connector ring used in joints in structural beams and laminated arches.

expansion and contraction to prevent cracking of the joints. For example, in a table using the mortise and tenon structure with rails, the top must be so held that it is free to move on the rails. In a table where the legs are fastened directly to the top, this provision is not needed.

With the same amount of glue area, edge grain and face grain make stronger joints than does the end grain. The high rate of swelling and shrinking across the end grain causes the joint to crack.

A glue joint is stronger than the surrounding wood, providing that it fits snugly and all surfaces are in contact. No space allowance is necessary for the adhesive.

A well-designed structure takes the grain direction into account when strength is important. The cross-grain strength of wood is expressed as the *modulus of rupture*, in pounds per square inch of cross-sectional area. For basswood this is approximately 10,000 pounds. The shearing strength, parallel to the grain, is only about 1,200 pounds. Consequently, when the grain runs crosswise in a slender section, it breaks easily. Woods generally are from five to fifteen times as strong across the grain as with it.

Usually the more glue area in a joint, the stronger that joint is. In the case of the mortise and tenon joint, there is a right relationship of glue area to wood cross-sectional area. The larger the tenon, the greater the glue area; but with a large tenon, the walls of the mortise become necessarily thin, with a loss of wood strength. For maximum strength in this joint, the cross-sectional area of the tenon should probably not exceed half of the total cross-sectional area of the piece.

The tongue and groove joint provides increased glue area for edge joining, and should make for a stronger joint, providing the tongue is in contact with the groove.

ANSWERS TO SOME PRACTICAL PROBLEMS (p. 152)

1. Compare the mechanisms of several different saws.
2. $3.52
3. $10.82
4. 690; 1,993; 2,300; 4,313
5. 25 sq. ft.
6. 147.4″
7. 2257.50 feet per minute
8. 1.74 lbs.
9. 37.5 per cent
10. 2 2/3 cups shellac; 1 1/3 cups alcohol

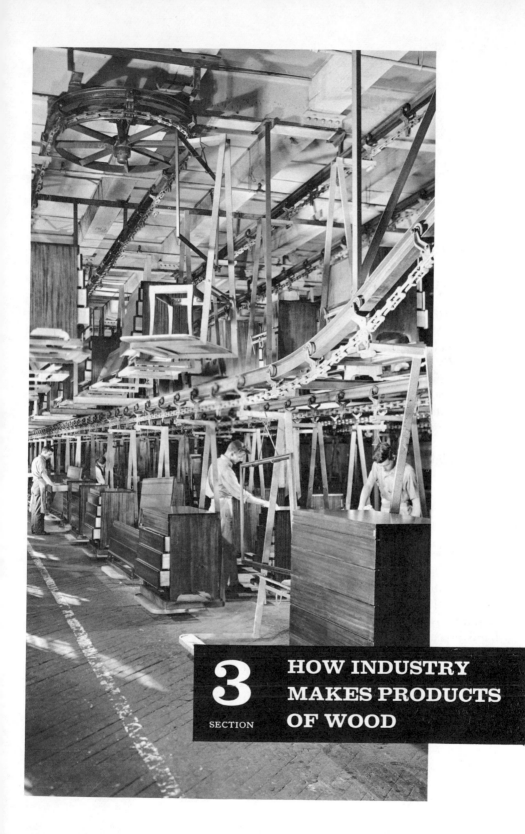

3

SECTION

HOW INDUSTRY MAKES PRODUCTS OF WOOD

WOODS AND THE MATERIAL CULTURE

Our *material culture* is the sum total of all we know and can do with materials. Wood was one of the first materials used by man. Probably first used as a club, when fastened to a rock it became a better club and later a hammer. When he discovered fire, man found that wood burned and gave off heat. And because he had wood for fuel, man learned to smelt copper and bronze.

Eventually, with a stone axe and with fire, man learned to hollow a log which would float in water and would enable him to carry things. When man made tools of metal, he could saw logs into slabs and boards with which to build boats and later, ships. With ships he discovered other lands and peoples and developed world commerce.

Meantime, man had learned that a log would roll. When it was sliced into discs, these rolled even better. These first wheels led to carts, then wagons, carriages, and automobiles. The first cars had wood frames and wheels.

The first material used for construction by our Pilgrims was wood. The log cabin is said to be the original American architecture.

For centuries, woodworking has been identified with hand work. But in the United States, technology has made production in wood as mechanical as man's ingenuity can make it. Many products still require hand processing, for by its nature, wood cannot be as easily formed as can metals, clay, or plastics, nor can pieces be fastened together as readily.

With modern chemistry, the natural qualities of wood are being improved. For example, experiments show it to be practical to plasticize wood so that it can be drawn or pressed into forms. This will make wood products manufacture more automatic than ever. Some predict that the future for wood is as a source of chemicals. The new materials derived in this way could be easily manufactured into many new products.

Today industry stands between the handcraft stage and automatic production. Experimenting with new techniques, it is at the same time keeping up production with hand- and machine-tool methods.

chapter 15

INDUSTRIAL
WOOD
PRODUCTS

In this chapter, the stories of the manufacturing of several common wood products are presented as typical illustrations of today's wood products production.

Boats.* Boat building is one of the most fascinating industries in the wood group. For many kinds of boats, wood is the preferred material. Ocean-going mine sweepers are made of wood because it is nonmagnetic. The famous P-T boats of World War II had hulls of plywood. Mahogany is one of the finest of woods for boats because of its natural resistance to water and weather. Oak and ash are commonly used for framing.

Models.** The manufacture of wood models of boats, ships, airplanes, and such has become one of the major industries supplying recreational needs.

Balsa is used for many of the parts because of its high ratio of strength to weight. Like all woods, balsa varies in density. The hard grade is used for structural framing, while the soft is used for covering, fairing, and such. Balsa is cut into model stock by slicing rather than by sawing. A sharp revolving disc slices it the way that bacon is sliced at the market.

Plywood and veneer are also used in models. Three-ply plywood in ⅟₁₆″, ⅜₂″,

* Prepared with the assistance of the Chris-Craft Corporation.

** Prepared with the assistance of the Dumas Model Company.

157

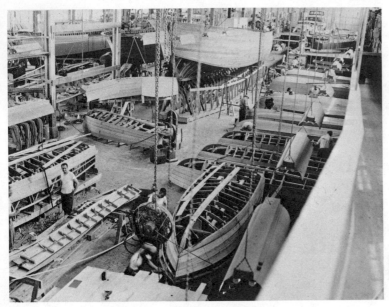

Fig. 15—1. Looking into a boat manufacturing plant. Many boats of different sizes are under construction at the same time.

Figs. 15—1 and 15—3 Courtesy The Chris-Craft Corporation

Fig. 15—2 (below, left, top). The structure of a model Chris-Craft cruiser is very similar to that of the full-size boat. Fig. 15—3 (below, left, bottom). This handsome 54-foot yacht is constructed almost entirely of wood. Fig. 15—4 (right). Parts for model boats are stamped onto a balsa wood sheet in a printing press.

Figs. 15—2 and 15—4 Courtesy Dumas Products, Inc.

and ⅛″ thicknesses, usually of birch, is especially adapted to model construction. Veneers are used for skin and covering. In manufacture, plywood parts are die-cut for precision and for quantity production. The sheet is inserted between the two halves of the steel die which, when pressed together, cut out the part.

Lead Pencils.* The lead pencil is a good example of a wood product that has been adapted to automatic production. The "lead" is really a mixture of

* Prepared with the assistance of the American Lead Pencil Co.

finely ground clay and graphite. This is shaped, sized, and bonded by baking. The leads are placed in grooves cut in slats of wood of pencil length and half pencil thickness. A similar slat is placed over the leads, and the two are glued together under hydraulic pressure into a pencil block.

The pencil blocks are then fed through a shaper which cuts the outside shape on both sides and divides the block into rough pencils. These are machine-sanded, enameled, stamped, and the ferrule is added. Thus the mystery of how the long hole is bored through a pencil is solved.

Fig. 15—5. Large planers flatten and surface assembled furniture panels.

Courtesy The Mengel Company

Fig. 15—6. The routing machine cuts intricate patterns in drawer and case fronts.

Courtesy The Mengel Company

Fig. 15—7. Making drawer parts. Molders form strips of wood into various shapes.

Courtesy The Mengel Company

Fig. 15—8. In the final assembly, drawers are hand-fitted.

Courtesy The Mengel Company

Furniture.* Today's furniture manufacturing is somewhat unusual. Designs of the past are being produced along with the latest in the contemporary, and often in the same factory. In this respect, furniture is unlike most other products. Clothing, automobiles, jewelry, and the like are styled for the present—the contemporary. But the greatest demand for furniture is still in the period styles rather than in the contemporary.

Larger furniture factories cure their own lumber and often have their own forests. After the design of the piece, or set of pieces, has been agreed upon,

the necessary tooling-up is done. The stock is then routed from one machine process to the next in the proper sequence by conveyors. Machine tools, such as saws and shapers, are set up to make single cuts, which are made on all of the stock before the setup is changed again.

Assembly is usually done by hand with the assistance of jigs and fixtures. Final sanding is a hand process, and finishing is generally done by hand spraying. In less expensive furniture, some of the hand work is eliminated by simplifying joinery and construction, omitting hand sanding, and so forth. Modern finishing materials make better finishes possible with less hand work.

* Prepared with the assistance of the Mengel Company.

Courtesy H. & A. Selmer, Incorporated

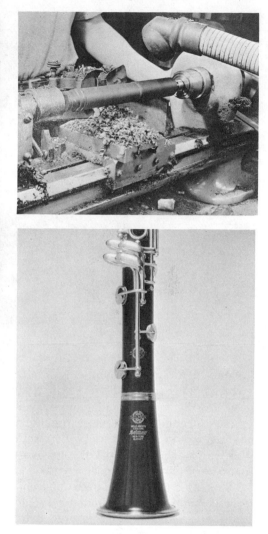

Fig. 15—9 (above). Clarinets illustrate the importance of seasoned wood. Grenadilla is aged for over a year at controlled temperatures and humidity. Fig. 15—10 (right, above). Grenadilla, so dense that it does not float in water, must be turned on a metalworking lathe. Fig. 15—11 (right). The product of painstaking workmanship in wood.

Clarinets.* The construction of wood clarinets is one of the most highly skilled of all crafts. Musicians prize this instrument over those of other materials because of its tone qualities.

Many different woods have been used, including rosewood and macassar, but

* *Prepared with the assistance of the G. Leblanc Corporation.*

grenadilla has been found to be most nearly ideal. It is least susceptible to shrinking and expanding, that natural characteristic of all woods. Grenadilla is obtained from the marshlands of remote Africa, and, like all woods, it varies in its characteristics. That selected for the finest clarinets is straight-grained and very dense. Seasoning takes as much as ten years. The wood is so hard it must be shaped by metalworking machine tools.

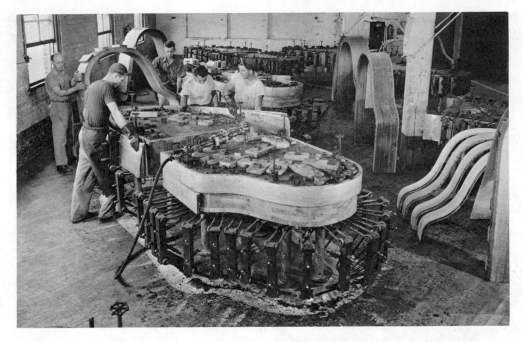

Both photos courtesy The Baldwin Piano Company

Pianos.* The grand piano still stands as one of the finest examples of craftsmanship in wood, and some will insist that it is the finest. From its impressively graceful cabinet, in a most functional styling, to the precise action of its keys, this instrument is a tribute to man's mastery of tools and woods.

Fig. 15—12 (above). Inner and outer rims of a grand piano are formed from laminated, cross-grained pieces. Fig. 15—13 (below). Hand rubbing.

The cabinet rim with its curved contour is made with a laminated construction. The individual sheets are coated with adhesive, assembled, and locked in a jig which produces the desired shape. The direction of the grain in the laminated construction is the same for each sheet—the long way of the stock.

The keyboard action is made of solid wood which must be light for easy working, yet strong and stiff to transmit the finger pressure to the hammers. The sounding board is made of solid wood.

* *Prepared with the assistance of the Baldwin Piano Company.*

Fig. 15—14 Courtesy U.S. Forest Service, Forest Products Laboratory. Fig. 15—15 Courtesy The Baldwin Piano Company

Fig. 15—14 (above). Many pieces are assembled to form the key action. Fig. 15—15 (below). Installing the key action.

Houses. * Within recent years the building of houses has gone industrial at a rapid rate. The pre-cut type is assembled on the foundation from parts cut to shape and size at the factory. Each part is numbered and keyed to a set of drawings to simplify the assembly, much the same as model airplanes and boats are built from kits.

The prefabricated house is partially assembled at the factory. Wall sections, for example, are built ready for assembly on the foundation. A small crew of men

Prepared with the assistance of National Homes.

can erect such a house in a matter of days.

In the manufacture of houses, machines are set up to process the total number of identical parts for perhaps dozens or even hundreds of houses. All of these parts are then routed to centers where they are selected and grouped for complete houses. A whole house is loaded into a truck or railroad car for delivery. One manufacturer assembles entire houses at the factory, even including carpeting. Each house is built in two or three sections which are trucked to the site and are placed on the foundation with huge cranes.

Fig. 15—16 (right). The foundation and floor slab are ready for the prefabricated home. Fig. 15—17 (below). Assembling the prefabricated wall panels. Insulation and windows are installed at the factory.

Both photos Courtesy National Homes, Incorporated

Fig. 15—18. The house is ready for roofing by the end of the day.

Courtesy National Homes, Incorporated

Structures.* The typical "carpentered" construction of toe-nailed butt joints has been used in small construction since the invention of the nail. The size and strength of such structures is limited, however, by this type of joinery. Imagination and research have devised methods of fastening wood together which have overcome these limitations and have opened new doors to possibilities for wood in large construction.

* Prepared with the assistance of The American Institute of Timber Construction.

Laminated construction involving the gluing of boards and planks into formed arches and straight beams is permitting the design of unique structures which can be prefabricated and shipped to the site. Assembly of the structure is simplified, functional design is emphasized, and the inherent characteristics of wood become part of the aesthetic quality of the building.

Laminating is done in huge jigs and presses. Glue is rolled on the stock as it is passed through the gluing machine. Then the pieces are assembled and clamped together to dry.

Fig. 15—19. The world's largest glued laminated wood arches are those of the Jai Alai Fronton Coliseum.

Courtesy Unit Structures, Incorporated

Figs. 15—20 and 15—22 Courtesy Timber Structures, Incorporated. Fig. 15—21 Courtesy Unit Structures, Incorporated

Fig. 15—20 (above, left). This unusual structure lends a simple dignity to a church. Note the sharp parabolic curves in the graceful arches. Fig. 15—21 (above, right). A high school gymnasium. Note the sturdiness of the arches, which at the same time are slender and graceful. Fig. 15—22 (below). The all-timber Loon Lake bridge, Roseburg, Oregon. Each wood part is chemically treated with preservatives before installation.

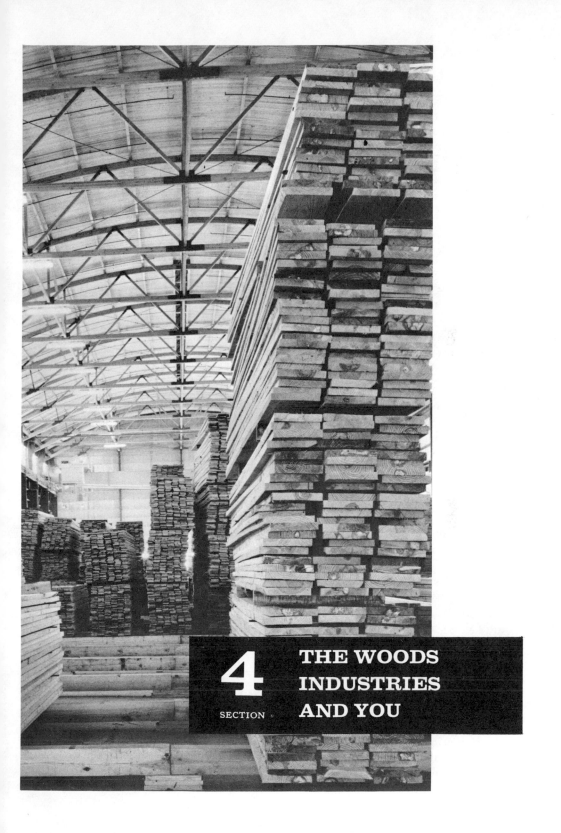

4

SECTION

THE WOODS
INDUSTRIES
AND YOU

chapter 16

RECREATION AND WOODS

What is there about woods and wood-working which might make them an exciting hobby for you? In answering this question you will find adventure, fun, and helpfulness. You might even become so expert at it that the hobby will lead to your life's work. It can happen that way.

To take a look at the hobby possibilities in woods, make a list of as many as you can think of. If each member of your class does the same and the ideas are combined, they will add up to dozens and dozens. You might start with the following list. See what you can add.

1. The home workshop
   a. Make your own workbench
   b. Make your own tool cabinet
2. Fix-it-for-fun
   a. Painting, decorating
   b. Repairing, refinishing furniture
3. Model design and construction
   a. Airplanes, boats, automobiles
   b. Furniture and home design
4. Crafts
   a. Whittling, carving, sculpture
   b. Wood burning
5. Processes
   a. Wood turning
   b. Jig sawing
6. Collecting
   a. Samples of woods, leaves
   b. Antiques
7. Jewelry
   a. Buckles
   b. Buttons
8. Toys
   a. Playthings
   b. Playground equipment
9. Farm
   a. Construction equipment
   b. Devising, inventing labor-savers
10. Community services
    a. Tree planting in parks and school grounds
    b. Bird feeders
11. Sports
    a. Archery bows, arrows
    b. Croquet sets

12. Camping
    a. Camping equipment
    b. Crafts
13. Tree farming
    a. Tree planting
    b. Tree identification
14. Business
    a. Manufacture of wood products
    b. Repairing of wood products

THE HOME WORKSHOP

Have you looked through a catalog lately at the dozens of tools and machines for working with wood and wished you had them in a home workshop? Or have you visited a large hardware store and drooled at them? Maybe you have wished that you had your industrial arts laboratory at home in your basement.

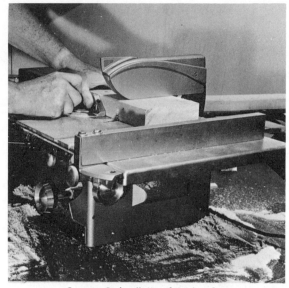

Courtesy Rockwell Manufacturing Company

Figs. 16—1, —2, —3. The three photographs on this page show a set of home-size power tools. The electric motors are built into the frames driving the tools directly. No belts are used. These are examples of machines made especially for the home workshop.

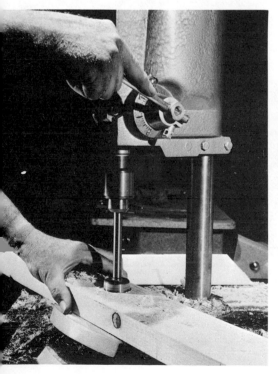

Suppose you are going to start building up a set of tools and machines for working with wood. If you can't get them all at once, what should you get first? You know from your work in industrial arts what the different tools and machines are for. So you would have to decide by what you want especially to do with wood. It all depends on what you want to be able to do and, of course, on how quickly you can get a full set.

Another problem: which should you get first, hand tools or machines? Some portable power tools cost little more than hand tools. Some one may recommend a jig saw as the first machine to buy; another person, a circular saw. Perhaps a workbench and a vise should come first. You could build such a bench in industrial arts. However you decide to go about equipping your home shop, you probably will want to get the most-used items first. This usually includes tools or machines for sawing, jointing straight edges, drilling and boring, nailing, and gluing.

THE AMERICAN CRAFTSMAN

Nearly all of the material things we use in living are mass produced in our great system of manufacturing industries. There are, however, individual craftsmen in every part of the country who are designing and constructing distinctively beautiful items in wood, clay, textiles, and other materials. Such pieces are usually one-of-a-kind. They are made by means of such tools and machines as described in this book. Sometimes the craftsman markets his own ware. A unique institution in New York City,

Courtesy America House

Fig. 16—4. A group of bowls, the rough gouging showing an imaginative respect for the natural wood grain. This treatment results in a unique product of fine craftsmanship. The set of servers combines the individuality of grain in wood with a simplicity of style.

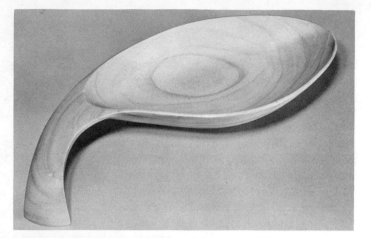

Fig. 16—5 (above). An unusual bowl sculptured from a single block of primavera wood. The Alaskan craftsman, George Fedoroff, in shaping the form to the pattern of the grain, has brought out the maximum natural beauty of the wood. Fig. 16—6 (left). The exotic graining of Siamese teakwood follows the curving shape of the two scoop servers handcrafted by Norwood Geague. His single server of Brazilian rosewood uses grain horizontal in the bowl but vertical in the twisted handle. Fig. 16—7 (below). Triangular bowl with handle handcrafted from lignum vitae, and African rosewood cheese board with ebony knife.

known as America House, encourages craftsmen to develop high quality products. It displays and sells these articles for the craftsmen. Study the examples shown here.

Do you like to design your own projects? If you do, try to find out why the work of such craftsmen-designers is outstanding. You need to know what makes an idea good. Who knows, there may be a profitable hobby or a career for you in creating fine ideas in wood.

Fig. 16—8 (above) and 16—9 (right). Two occasional tables, splendid examples of simplicity of design taking full advantage of beautiful wood grain. Fig. 16—10 (below). A wall-hung chest of drawers by Phillip Lowell Powell and Paul Evans. The graining and burl of the black walnut provides the decoration on the front. A small overhang on each drawer serves as the finger-tip pull.

All photographs on this page Courtesy America House

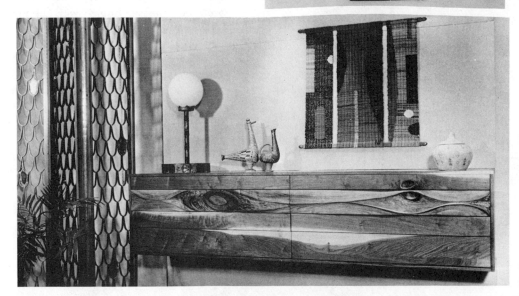

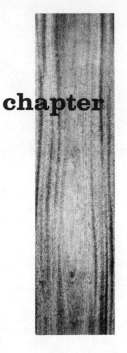

chapter 17

OCCUPATIONS IN THE WOOD INDUSTRIES

The chart "Products of American Industries" (see p. 125) not only classifies the thousands of wood products and uses but provides some clues as to the nature of occupations in the woods products manufacturing industries. In addition to such occupations are those in the fields of forestry and soil conservation in county, state, and national government. Tree surgery, too, has opportunities. Prepare a list of all the occupations you can find in woods industries. Look into the sources of information listed in Resource Material (see p. 252-253).

It is possible that you may discover an occupation in your searching that has particular appeal to you. If so, search out all possible information on it so that you can better decide whether or not it really is for you. No matter where your vocational interests lie, it is a good idea to narrow your choices down to a few as soon as you can in your high school career. Then proceed to find out all you can about each. The best way to

decide on your choices is to get a job, perhaps part time, in this kind of activity and actually try it out. Your industrial arts activities will give you experiences related to wood products design and manufacturing. If your class gets into the manufacture of an item on a production basis, you will get some real industrial-type experiences.

The future of the woods industries is as unlimited as that of any other. Chemists, engineers, architects, research workers, and technicians are needed as much here as in other industries. In fact, if you graduate from college in one of these fields, you will probably be qualified for work in most American industries.

There was a time about 25 years ago when it appeared that our wood supply would soon be exhausted. Consequently it was felt that wood products would soon be replaced by other materials. Today it is easy to see how wrong these predictions were. Research, engineering, and imagination have found so many new uses for wood that thousands of jobs have been made which were unheard of 25 years ago.

A recent study of the United States Department of Commerce Census of Manufactures reveals that there are more than 42,000 establishments in the country engaged in manufacturing products of wood and in logging and saw mill operations. The number of people employed is nearly 800,000.

Employment figures in the wood products manufacturing industries showed a decline for several years prior to 1958. What does this mean for the occupational possibilities? It means that certain types of jobs are being taken over by machines, that machines are eliminating certain jobs. It also means that with research, new uses for wood are being found; and although these often mean new jobs, they require new skills. Now that most of the tree goes into chemicals, this opens up an entire field of occupations. And this area continues to grow while the other declines.

Among the unemployed in the country at present, approximately two-thirds have not completed high school. With the rapid technological change going on, a young man entering industry today can expect to change his job at least four to five times during his work life. Consequently, he will need frequent retraining. With such job changes, the level of

Fig. 17—1 (top, right). The cypress everglades in Florida provide initial employment in logging. This leads to many related occupational opportunities. Fig. 17—2 (bottom, right). An industrial furniture worker in Maine.

Top photograph courtesy Florida State News Bureau. Bottom, courtesy Maine Department of Economic Development

Courtesy North Carolina News Bureau

Fig. 17—3. In the United States, we presently use an average of 30,154,000 tons of paper yearly, 300 pounds per person. Besides newsprint and book papers, the paper industry supplies roofing felt, wallboard, and asbestos papers for building, wrapping papers, stationery, absorbent papers, cartons and containers. Through chemistry, paper is made stronger, fireproof, resistant to water and acids.

qualifications for the new jobs goes higher. Your best insurance is a skill that is needed whether it is as a craftsman, a technician, or other—and don't overlook the opportunities in industrial arts teaching. But a high school diploma is the first requisite.

If you do not go on to higher education, it may be all the more important for you to prepare for a skilled occupation such as that of a craftsman or tradesman. Talk to your teacher about an apprenticeship.

Your future is up to you. Try to decide where you want to be 20 years from now, then plan accordingly. With such a goal before you, all of your school work will become more interesting. You won't have much spare time either, because you will want to do things that are related to your chosen field. The tough problem is to decide on a vocation while you are still in school. Talk this over with your industrial arts teacher. He knows about a great many industrial occupations, and he can tell you about opportunities for being an industrial arts teacher, too. Maybe he can help you to get some try-out experience either in your industrial arts class or after school. Remember, there is not one, but dozens of occupations for which you can become well qualified, in which you can find happiness, and through which you can do much good.

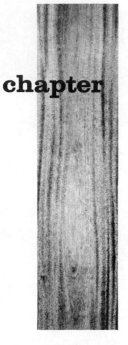

chapter **18**

THE CONSUMER
AND WOOD
PRODUCTS

All of the information in this book has value for the consumer as he selects, uses, and evaluates wood in its many forms and products. It serves him in selection, use, and purchase of tools, machines, and supplies for working with wood. Following are ten groups of questions with which the intelligent consumer is concerned. Use them as topics for discussion and bases for evaluating choices when purchasing. Use them also as a check list for judging projects.

1. Function
   How well does it accomplish its purpose?
   Does it operate easily, simply?
   Is the relationship of size to function adequate?
2. Structure
   Is it structurally sound, sensible, imaginative?

Is construction appropriate to function and materials?
Are parts replaceable?
3. Durability
   Will it function as long as desired?
   Is it too durable?
   Is the surface finish permanent?
4. Materials
   Are appropriate materials involved?
   Are the materials repairable?
   Could less expensive materials be as satisfactory?
5. Aesthetic
   Does its beauty originate within itself?
   Will it promote harmony within its environment?
   Will it show the purchaser to be a person of good taste?
6. Economic
   Is it a sound investment?
   Is depreciation a factor?

Which is wiser, to repair the old or replace it?

7. Cultural

Does it reflect the best in the past?

Does it effectively reflect the contemporary spirit?

Does it make a unique contribution, or is it more of the same?

8. Social

What effect will its possession have on others?

How may it reflect on its owner?

Does it set a pattern, or follow one?

9. Safety

Is it protected—electrically or chemically—from dirt, deterioration?

Is the operator protected: guards, dust, fumes, shock?

Is it sturdy enough?

10. Personal

Is the purchaser happy with it; will he recommend it?

Does it give him pride of possession?

Does it make his living more enjoyable, and work lighter?

Is it comfortable and convenient?

CONSUMER PROJECTS

It will be easier to see how important the above consumer's check points are if you undertake some group projects such as those that follow. By such activities you may be able also to inform other students, especially those who are not taking industrial arts, about the usefulness of these evaluations.

1. Using several models of student-made tables, chairs, and so forth, have a group meeting to judge them critically on a functional basis. Try to demonstrate the functional efficiency of each.

2. Make up a sample group of joints which may be used in fastening a leg to a table. Try to exhaust the possibilities. Devise metal supports as well as wooden. Test them for sturdiness and practicality, and then rate them good, better, best, or by other grades.

3. Cut some test blocks of several kinds of woods and mount them on a rack out of doors. Leave them exposed for a full school year and then note the comparative resistances to weather.

4. Take another such set of wood samples and apply several different finishes, including house paint, enamel, lacquer, shellac, wax, and others. Expose these to the weather also and note the effects on the finishes as well as the protection afforded the woods.

5. With several samples of the same kind of wood try a number of different finishes to see which is most effective in bringing out the natural beauty of the grain and the color.

6. Visit a museum to analyze the design quality as well as the structural details of early furniture. If possible, visit a museum of modern art, too, to make a comparative study of contemporary furniture. Perhaps the owner of a furniture store will let you study his merchandise during an evening or on a closed day when you would not interfere with sales.

7. Perhaps your group could redesign the seats in a classroom emphasizing function, convenience, comfort, and so forth. Study the present seats for all possible weaknesses and then redesign to eliminate or minimize the faults. You could try this on your shop work benches, too.

8. Conduct a public opinion poll among the students in your school

for purposes of determining which design is preferred among all of the coffee tables, personal desks, or other models of projects produced in your class. Determine preferences of the girls as compared with those of the boys, and then study the chosen pieces to see if you can find why they are preferred.

9. Visit a lumber yard to find what kinds of wood are available, their sources, costs, and common uses. Compare costs by kinds of lumber, dimension, and quality.

10. Visit a tree farm, nursery, or national forest to see how seedlings are grown and planted, how insects and disease are controlled, and how fires are prevented. Then, if you possibly can, plant a tree yourself; protect it, and watch it grow. Someday you will be very proud of it.

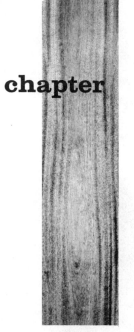

chapter 19

DESIGN IN WOOD

Nature has furnished more than a thousand kinds of trees from which man can get wood. Man himself has invented and produced at least as many tools, machines, and processes for converting wood into useful products. So, your teacher can say to you, "Here are many kinds of woods and here are the tools and machines to shape them. Now, what will you do with them?"

Should you do only what someone else has done? Or should you search for better ideas than someone else has had? In our country every one is free to develop better ideas than have been used. This is especially true in American industry where the goal is always better ideas. No matter how good products are, industry is constantly searching for better ones.

No product is so good that it cannot be improved or replaced by a better one. This is the spirit that spurs the designer on to greater things and makes living for all of us more interesting. If it weren't for that spirit, we in America would be living in log cabins and sod shanties just as the first pioneers did. There would be no air travel, no television, no highways, no penicillin, no plastics, no rubber, no automatic machines—none of the millions of products that have been developed since those days. Apply this to yourself in your industrial arts class and you will want to learn how to design with materials, because then you, too, can put into form the ideas you have. You will have an opportunity to show what *you* can do.

WHAT IS DESIGNING?

Designing is thinking expressed in materials instead of in words.

Designing begins with a problem. That problem may be to produce a better chair, for example; to make a kind of chair that has not existed before; to change a chair so that it can be made more economically, or to make a chair from new materials. Designing makes use of creating, planning, searching, inventing, and constructing in the quest for more effective solutions to problems. Designing is a selective process in which poor and mediocre ideas are discarded in favor of good ones. A designer does not settle for the first idea he gets; he looks at a great many before he decides. If you haven't had much experience in designing, you will probably be amazed at what you can do when you are given a chance to be creative and the responsibility for it, along with some help from your teacher and your classmates.

WHAT IS GOOD DESIGN?

Good design in a product and in a project made in industrial arts are the same; good design is good anywhere. It does not vary from one country to the next, nor from one generation to the other. Good design is not dated; it is not faddish; it does not go out of style. Good design is much more than attractive decoration and pleasing color combinations. Good design originates with a good idea; it is good thinking. The following qualities of good design can be used in judging any project or product. Consider them carefully.

Function. Good design grows out of an analysis of the function of the article. Good design means that the piece has purpose and that it accomplishes this purpose well. It has usefulness and a reason for being.

Function itself assumes several forms. A project may have as its purpose, for example, to hold a door open. This is a

Fig. 19—1. A Danish contemporary easy chair of ash. Note the segmented foam cushions which follow the contour of the back. Clever?

Courtesy Heywood-Wakefield and Hedrich-Blessing Studio

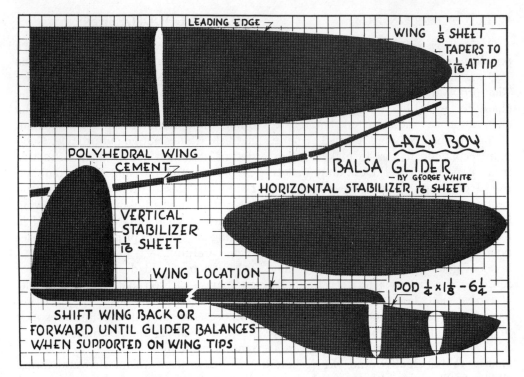

Fig. 19—2. A hand-launched glider. In design of this type, which reflects aero-dynamic principles, beauty originates in the forms necessary to the function of the glider.

lowly chore, without glamor or attention. On the other hand, the purpose of a wood carving may be to be beautiful, to satisfy one's liking for the aesthetic. It might not serve any other function, yet this is sufficient.

Once the function of a project has been decided on, then its form becomes important because it is that which enables the piece to perform its function. The relationship of the two may be expressed as "form follows function." This means that the actual form or shape of the object should originate in its function and should reflect that function. If you see an axe handle by itself, its form suggests that you grip it. The

same occurs with a ball bat, but they cannot be used interchangeably very well. The form of the axe handle suggests a different type of swing than does the bat.

Durability. The most durably built product is not necessarily the best in design. Take paper plates, for instance. They are intended to be used once and then to be discarded; and because they are expendable they must be inexpensive. Clay, glass, metal, or plastic plates are much more durable, but will not serve the purpose of disposable picnic plates as well. A project or product should be only as durable as it needs to be to serve its purpose. If it is built to last a hundred years, it will obviously be quite different from a product or project built to last but a few hours. Most industrial arts students overdo this feature of durability, with the result that projects often appear clumsy, complicated, cluttered, and crude. A knowledge of materials and structures is needed if one is to get just the proper emphasis on durability, so that the piece does not appear to be too strong, too durable.

Economy. Economy does not mean cheapness; it means that the project should be so designed that a minimum of waste is incurred—a minimum of waste of time and labor, as well as of materials. If you design two equally functional and beautiful tables—but one can be made at half the cost of the other—the less expensive one will probably be considered the better in design. Wise selection of materials and simple structure will keep the project economical.

Materials. The project should be made of materials that are most suitable and appropriate to function, durability, and economy. Wood is wood, but all woods are not equally suitable for the same uses. Balsa and black walnut, for example, have very little in common, yet each can be the best choice of material for certain purposes. You can turn a ball bat from white pine, but you can't hit a home run with it.

Courtesy Sprague and Carleton

Fig. 19—3. An American colonial setting. This was the type of furniture made in the Colonies for the working class of people.

Construction. Structurally a project should make good sense. Methods of construction should be appropriate to function, durability, economy, and, of course, materials. A butt joint may be the best structure to use in one case; in another, a mortise and tenon. The simpler the construction in keeping with the other factors, the better. Let the construction lend interest to the piece. It is not necessary to conceal the joinery. If you study the fine examples of contemporary Scandinavian woodwork you will see that they are especially fascinating because construction is considered a part of the design; it is not a necessary evil to be tolerated but concealed. The simple, logical construction employed makes the piece easy to understand, and consequently, to appreciate.

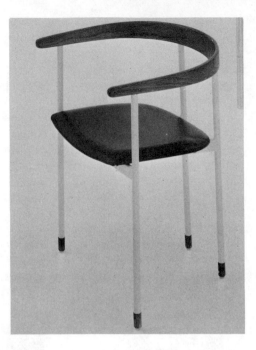

Danish contemporary combines strength and comfort with lightness in weight. It uses teak, walnut, and ash as the common woods, but employs many different materials along with wood. In Fig. 19—4 (above) the chair back is steamed ash. The legs are steel tube and seat is cushioned with foam. The base of the table below (Fig. 19—5) is painted steel.

Both photographs courtesy Heywood-Wakefield and Hedrich-Blessing Studio

Personality. If a product is particularly interesting, the chances are that the designer has woven some of his own personality into it. This quality is hard to define, but easy to detect. Two book racks can be equally functional, durable, and economical, but one may be far more interesting to look at because of clever personal touches worked in by the designer. He may have combined other materials, such as metals, textiles, or reed. He may have shaped the legs in an unusual manner. He may have done any of a great number of things to it that make it particularly appealing and out of the ordinary. This quality of personality makes the article intriguing and fascinating. We wonder *who* did it. This quality, then, gives the article a feeling of humanness which machine-made products often lack. Your big challenge in project design is likely to be: how to keep it from being ordinary.

Beauty. A product is most beautiful when its form has grown out of its function, when the proper degree of durability has been included, when economy is apparent, when its materials are appropriate, when its construction is logical and simple, and when the personality of the designer is evident in it. All of this means that beauty is not something added to a product or a project after it has been designed. Beauty is integral. A beautiful design has a pleasing combination of all the qualities of design. Its lines, curves, masses, colors, textures, and finish are effectively handled with the result that the product has appeal to one's natural desire for the beautiful.

Fig. 19—6. A Danish modern setting. This style combines simple shapes and structures, generally of solid woods. Open construction, as in the couches shown, requires very accurate workmanship.

Courtesy Heywood-Wakefield

Courtesy The Karges Furniture Company, Incorporated

Fig. 19—7. Louis XVI connoisseur's cabinet. This is an outstanding example of today's craftsmanship in period furniture. Interestingly, this cabinet is truly international. The idea originated in France. An Italian master carver fashioned the lower door panels by hand. But the carving at the top was done in Evansville, Indiana, on a multiple machine carver. The brass grill was cast in Florence, Italy. Some of the wood is Circassian walnut from behind the Iron Curtain. The entire cabinet, however, is an American production item.

GOOD DESIGN IN WOOD

The general qualities of good design apply to wood products and projects as they do to all others. However, there are some specific design suggestions particularly applicable to wood.

1. A project of wood should look as if it is made of wood. It is not design wise to try to imitate a different material. Honesty is important in project design.
2. Do not use wood when another material would make better design sense. For example, making something of wood that properly should be of metal just to show that one can do it, is not good design sense.
3. Select a wood that best suits the project, considering function, durability, economy, construction, and beauty.
4. Make sure the hardware adds to the beauty of the piece rather than detracts.
5. The boldest grain pattern may not be the most beautiful after finishing. It may be too "noisy."
6. Use appropriate fastening devices. Use no more of them than necessary for the desired durability. Align screw slots with the grain of the wood.
7. Natural finishes usually bring out the most beauty in wood. But because a wood is finished naturally does not necessarily make it beautiful. Staining one wood to imitate another tends to destroy the feeling of genuineness and honesty that is characteristic of good design. If you want a walnut finish, use walnut wood.
8. Fine, careful workmanship makes the piece all the more beautiful.
9. Wood has a warmth, a friendliness, and a charm about it because it comes from trees which people see as living beauty. The challenge to the designer is to draw on these natural attributes of wood and make them apparent in his handiwork.

HOW TO DESIGN PROJECTS IN WOOD

The procedure you can use in designing is much the same as that of the industrial designer. Follow these suggestions:

1. Decide on the purpose, the function of the project. What is it for? Whom will it serve? Where will it be used? What form should it have to serve its purpose well?
2. Search for ideas. How have other people solved this problem? What good ideas have they used? Which of these suggest other ideas to you? Make many sketches.
3. Experiment with mechanisms, unusual structures and the like when they are needed. Build scale models to test these features.
4. Determine the over-all size. What length, width, and height are best, considering the function? Figure out the best proportions between these dimensions. Make a scale drawing (full-size is preferred).
5. Add the functional details, such as drawers, shelves, and doors. Arrange order and position effectively.
6. Check your proposal with your teacher and with several people to see if it has any weaknesses. Then make changes in the drawing if necessary.
7. Construct a scale model (full-size when feasible) and get criticisms from several people. Make any changes you feel are necessary, and

note the effect. Changes are not always improvements.

8. Make a working drawing of the project and any full-size patterns needed. Figure the cost of the project from a bill of materials. List the step-by-step procedure for constructing the project. Have your teacher go over your drawing and patterns, costs, and schedule with you.

   When the drawing is complete with dimensions, number each part on the drawing for identification. Give each sub-assembly a letter designation as A, B, C, etc. Then each part in a sub-assembly is numbered as A-1, A-2, B-1, and so on. In compiling the parts list, or bill of material, include the part number, name, finished dimensions, material, and number required.

9. Make a full-size *pilot* model of inexpensive wood when necessary to make sure of the design.

10. Construct the project. Let it then receive a thorough judging by several people and by a professional designer if possible. Decide on how it might be improved if you were to make another.

BEAUTY AND WOOD

Even though many woods are beautiful in grain pattern, color and texture, projects made from them are not necessarily beautiful. The problem is how not to lose the natural beauty of the wood and how to make it even more beautiful. It takes more than material to make a project attractive. There are several factors that must be taken into account to produce an article with good aesthetic quality. As you study them, you will see how they are woven into the various qualities of good design already described.

Form. It has been pointed out that the form of an object should be determined by its function. Form is defined by lines and curves that give shape to areas (two-dimensional figures having only length and width), and masses (three-dimensional figures). In some cases, such as a coffee table, the form of the top might be rectangular, square, circular, angular, or free form and each could serve the purpose equally well. The choice of shape then can be determined by the environment in which the table will be placed, by the personal preferences of the designer, or even by the grain pattern of the wood itself.

Proportion. Proportion is the relationship of these dimensions and is expressed as an actual ratio. When, for instance, the length of a desk top is 48 inches and the width, 28, the ratio is 28/48 or 7/12. Odd ratios such as this are generally more preferable than even ones. 1/3, 1/5, 2/3, 3/5, and so forth are odd, and 1/2, 1/4, and so forth are even. When proportion is well handled, a project has a feeling of gracefulness. When poorly handled, it seems clumsy.

Balance. Balance means a state of equilibrium in physics as well as in design. For design purposes, however, balance may be actual or it may be apparent. When a design is arranged about a center line so that the halves are identical, it has *symmetrical balance*. When the parts are so arranged that the balance cannot actually be measured, but yet one gets the feeling that they are in balance, the piece has *informal* or *asymmetrical balance*. You can tell by

THE DESIGN PROCESS APPLIED

THE PROBLEM: TO DESIGN A SIMPLE, FUNCTIONAL BOOK RACK.

THE SPECIFICATIONS: HOLD 6-10 BOOKS; TO SIT ON TABLE OR SHELF; TO KEEP BOOKS FROM FALLING OVER. THE TYPICAL BOOK RACK IS FAULTY.

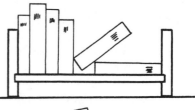

AN IDEA FOR A SOLUTION: RAISE ONE END AND THE BOOKS DO NOT FALL OVER.

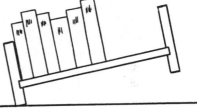

MODIFICATION: LOWER ONE END TO THE TABLE.

REFINEMENT: SIMPLIFIES AND BEAUTIFIES.
STEP I. REMOVE UNNECESSARY MATERIAL.

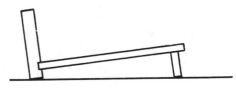

STEP II. TAPERING ELIMINATES EXCESS WEIGHT, ADDS GRACEFULNESS.

STEP III. SCULPTURING (STREAMLINING) EMPHASIZES THE BEAUTY OF THE WOOD; ADDS FEELING OF FINE CRAFTMANSHIP, RICHNESS AND OVERALL BEAUTY.

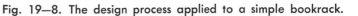

Fig. 19—8. The design process applied to a simple bookrack.

looking at an object whether it is well balanced or not. When well-balanced, it is neither top-heavy, bottom-heavy, nor lopsided.

Emphasis. A design without emphasis is like a story without a plot, a joke without a point. The dominant part of the design is the part which is the "design story." All other parts are subordinate to it, but necessary; they help to get the point across. In a well-designed television console, the dominant part is the screen. The wood, the finish, the hardware, and all the rest do not compete with the screen for attention—they lend emphasis to the purpose of the object. Whenever the parts in a design compete with one another, the entire result is disturbing.

Unity. A feeling of unity or oneness is essential to beauty in design. When all the parts seem to get along well with each other, there is unity. When one's eye can move smoothly around the design instead of having to jump from one element to another, there is unity.

Rhythm. A feeling of rhythm in a design is obtained by *repetition* of forms, lines, curves, colors, textures, and the like. Rhythm produces a feeling of pleasing motion as the eye looks over the object. Without such motion a design seems static, asleep, dead. *Variety* is introduced to prevent excessive repetition and the monotony it produces. This works in the way that a dash of salt or pepper can add flavor to food and make it more appealing to one's taste.

Fig. 19–9. The solid black walnut here incorporated influences from Brazil and the Mediterranean area. Note the sleek, slender lines and the use of the inverted arches. This is a splendid example of the effectiveness of rhythm.

Courtesy American Walnut Manufacturers' Association

Texture. Texture refers to the quality of the surface of a material, as coarse or fine, rough or smooth, bold or subdued, regular or free. The beauty of a material and of a project is often enhanced by emphasizing texture. Wood is almost always sanded as smoothly as possible, so you may have gotten the idea that smoothness is correct. However, some woods take on a most unusual character when their surfaces are deliberately roughened. Look for some sandblasted Douglas Fir at the lumber yard. Try a "sugi" cypress finish yourself. See what quality a piece of mahogany takes on when it is brushed with a wire scratch wheel. Coarse textures are excellent dust catchers and should be used only when appropriate.

Harmony. This quality is closely related to unity in that it results only when all of the elements in the design get along well together. When there is harmony, there is the oneness of unity, and a pleasing over-all effect. When harmony is overdone, a feeling of monotony and inactivity may result. Then the design becomes "too much the same" and lacks appeal and interest.

Color. Color selection is important in all designing. There are principles that simplify the selection and use of color in all types of designing, but when applied to wood projects they need special study. The selection of wood according to color is often ignored in industrial arts. A student likes black walnut so he makes all of his projects of it. Another may attempt

Fig. 19—10. A buffet in Danish contemporary with a hutch top. The designer has incorporated woven cane for a variety. This gives the piece a personal touch, too. Woods get along well with other natural fibers. The square edges have been slightly rounded and softened, but not to a full half-circle, which would have spoiled the effect.

Courtesy Heywood-Wakefield

Fig. 19—11. An American-made table reflecting Oriental influence. The fretwork effect of the square scrolls, the straight lines, the blocky, massive structure, and the black lacquer finish suggest Chinese and Indian influence.

to improve on Nature's color by bleaching the wood, and another may stain one wood to look like another. If we are to take color seriously in woodwork, let us give thought to these suggestions.

1. When selecting wood for a project, consider its natural color when finished. Will it harmonize with other furniture in the room? Should it harmonize, or would it be better for it to contrast with the rest? If it is to be a center of interest, a conversation piece, in the room, perhaps it should contrast.

2. Different colors of woods suggest different feelings. The deep brown of walnut suggests formality, solemnity, dignity, and richness. The gay red of mahogany suggest warmth, friendliness, cheerfulness, royalty. The deep, mellow red-brown of black cherry suggests hominess, simplicity, charm. Hard maple lends a feeling of light-ness, femininity, casualness. Study other woods to see if you can read traits of character into them.

3. If two or more woods of different colors are combined, make one of them dominant. To do this, use more of it; make it the center of interest. Avoid extremes in contrast, such as in the combination of maple with black walnut. Such contrast can cheapen the effect, making the project gaudy. Very few turned projects of laminated maple and walnut can be classed as good design on the basis of color alone.

4. In transparent finishes, the addition of a slight bit of the right color of stain can truly enhance the beauty of a wood. For example, darkening maple slightly emphasizes the subtle grain pattern and tones down the glaring whiteness. This treatment requires much experimenting because

it is so easily overdone. Mahogany is commonly dyed so deeply that the grain pattern is actually concealed. Most woods darken with age after finishing. This should be allowed for. Your teacher may have some samples of wood which show this mellowing.

5. The chances are that you won't improve on Nature's coloring of her woods with your stains, filler, and bleaches until you have studied and experimented for years. Consequently use such chemicals sparingly if you want the most pleasing results, results that will be pleasing now and years later as well. It makes better sense to select the kind of wood to give the desired effect at the start, rather than to try to "doctor" it when the project is completed.

SURFACE ENRICHMENT

There are times when the surface of the wood may be enhanced by decorative treatment other than that of natural color and finish. The common techniques include painted-on designs, freehand or stencil, carving in its many forms, inlaying with special veneers, overlaying with glued-on forms, and many others. The question to be answered in each case is, will the decoration really enhance the project? If it does, it will look as though it belongs there; that it is better to have it than not to have it; that it seems related to the piece and appears to be a part of it. Truly fine design needs little added surface enrichment; but when well-handled, it does contribute to the beauty and the personality and never interferes with function. The tendency for a beginner in adding such decoration is to overdo it. Get the opinions of several competent people. They can help you to decide if your plans for surface decoration are in good taste and desirable.

FURNITURE STYLES

Furniture can be identified by *styles*, sometimes called *periods*. In a large furniture store you may find pieces grouped according to whether they are Colonial, Empire, Renaissance, Contemporary, Danish Modern, or other style. There is considerable difference in construction as well as appearance. A style begins with a particular design created by someone and then widely accepted and copied. Some early styles originated with European royalty. Kings

Fig. 19–12. An airchair in today's Danish manner. There is no excess material in this piece. It gets its strength in its design and structure. Note the arm which has been sculptured from the arm stock, showing that wood is readily adaptable to its tasks. The challenge for the designer is to make fullest use of wood's "talents."

Courtesy DUX, Incorporated. Design by Folke Ohllsson

Fig. 19—13 (above). American-made dining room furniture, showing the traditional influence in design. The chairs reflect the Hepplewhite and the splayed-leg table the Chippendale influences. Fig. 19—14 (below). American contemporary dining room setting in solid walnut. Simple forms and lines and a dependence on the natural beauty of the wood characterize this style.

Fig. 19—13 Courtesy The Mengel Company. Fig. 19—14 Courtesy American Walnut Manufacturers' Association

and queens had their own personal cabinet makers, weavers, carvers, and other highly skilled craftsmen. Obviously, furniture designed for a king was the finest, and lesser people could do no better than to copy it. Such names as Jacobean, Queen Anne, and Louis XVI identify different styles of such furniture. You can see examples in museums.

Early architects and cabinet makers started furniture styles, too. The Adam brothers, Hepplewhite, Sheraton, and Chippendale are but a few of them. Their names are now attached to styles of furniture which they designed for wealthy clients.

Today we use such terms as Colonial, Early American, and Contemporary to identify general styles. Colonial refers to the furniture made during the period of American colonization and used then in the homes of the common people. Early American is a broad class of furniture made in Revolutionary days as the furniture industry got under way. Period furniture includes the many styles that originated in Europe, particularly in the 18th and 19th centuries. Contemporary is that which reflects the design thinking of today. It makes no ties with the past. The form and construction is simple and plain. Its form follows the function and it is easily adapted to mass production.

Scandinavian contemporary furniture is popular today, especially Danish and Swedish. The use of solid woods in sculptured, slender, clean forms with simple, open construction makes it distinctive. Italian modern is distinctive by contrast with the Scandinavian. Many materials are used including iron, brass, marble, glass, and wood. Several are often combined in a single piece of furniture. The effect is very decorative.

FOR RESEARCH, EXPERIMENT, DEVELOPMENT

1. Who are some of today's well-known professional furniture designers?
2. Why is contemporary Scandinavian style furniture preferred by many Americans?
3. Why is there not one American style of furniture which we all use?
4. Which is more important for most industrial arts students, skill in thinking or skill in wood processing?
5. Why is American black walnut the favorite cabinet wood in this country?
6. How can a project be kept from being ordinary?
7. Why does the shape of a claw hammer or an axe handle not change?
8. Which brings out the natural beauty of wood better, a surface finish or a penetrating finish?
9. Why is an analysis of function a logical beginning for the design of a product or a project?
10. Why are designs rarely perfect for all time; and why are they usually perfect, if they are, for now only?

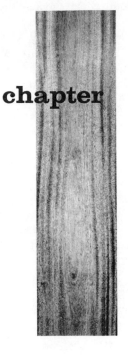

chapter 20

YOUR WOODWORKING PROJECT

The purpose of the project is to give you practical experience in thinking, reasoning, solving problems, creating, inventing, planning, and researching with ideas and materials. You express your ideas in materials rather than with words. Consequently, the project is much more than just "something to make."

What you do in the way of projects in woodworking is mighty important. In the first place, your own personality shows in each thing you make. Everyone can "see" you in your projects. How do you want them to see you? Secondly, the time you spend on a project can never be replaced. It seems, therefore, that it should show you off at your best. Here are some things to think and talk about as you consider the projects you will make.

1. *A project can serve as a monument to its builder.*
   a. How can one tell when good thinking has been used in a project?
   b. Why does a lazy person make a lazy-looking project?
   c. If one is afraid to be different, what type of projects will he choose to make?
   d. How can one see that imagination has been used in a project?
   e. How can the project show that the student has confidence in himself?
   f. How does one's attitudes toward honesty show up in a project?
   g. How do hidden talents show?
   h. How can one tell that the project represents the very best that the maker could do at the time?

2. *When you choose your own project, you are responsible for making a good choice.*

   a. Why should you be permitted to choose your own projects?

   b. How can you know when your choice is a good one?

   c. Should you be expected to come through with the project when you have chosen it?

   d. When a student insists on making a project exactly like one made by someone else, what may this mean? If one copies somebody's project or plan, his project is second-handed. Design and make your own. Then it will be first-hand and your interest in it will probably keep it first-rate.

3. *What the student does to the project is important, but what it does to him is even more important.*

   a. Why should each succeeding project provide new experiences for the student?

   b. Of what value is a "busy work" project?

   c. Why is a simple design more difficult to work out than a complicated one?

   d. Suppose you miss your measurements on a piece, what should you do? Fill in the gap with wood putty? Hide the piece and get a new one?

   e. Suppose someone laughs at your idea or your project? Should you get angry? Feel insulted? Ignore it? Laugh too?

   f. What difference does it make when you really "love" your project?

4. *The only alternative to careful planning is extra work and extra expense.*

   a. What does planning in a project mean?

   b. How can one solve problems before they happen?

   c. Why does planning seem painful to some people?

   d. Is there only one right way to go about a project, or are there several?

   e. How can you tell when you have planned wisely?

PRODUCTION PROJECTS

A production project is our means of producing quantities of identical items. And as we do this, we gain an understanding of manufacturing industries. We meet up with real problems similar to those that industries face.

We cannot manufacture our products exactly as industry would do it because we are not an industry. The machines in most industrial arts woods laboratories are machine tools rather than industrial production machines. However, we can adapt our machine tools for production by means of jigs. These enable us to produce identical parts by holding material in the proper position for processing on a machine.

In a production project we can study a manufacturing industry. We know that the production of the item is not the whole story of that industry. There is the economic side, too. If the sale of a product does not result in a profit, an industry cannot stay in business. A means for marketing the product, good management, and efficient labor are all necessary for an industry to be maintained and to grow.

A small group of students or the whole class can involve itself in a production project. It may include the invitation of industrial experts to visit your class and tell you how industry does it. Here are some typical problems you will meet in any such project. Discuss them in advance and propose solutions. Visit an actual plant and study the organization of a manufacturing industry.

1. The selection of the article to be produced.
2. The design and refinement of the article to eliminate all possible handwork.
3. The design of structures to simplify production.
4. The tooling-up. Design and construction of jigs and fixtures, special tools, and so forth.
5. The selection of materials and supplies.
6. The scheduling of production and determination of jobs involved.
7. The manufacturing processes involved.
8. Inspection technique and devices.
9. Assembly sequences and methods.
10. Methods for finishing and type of finish.
11. Provision for re-work.
12. Means for advertising and public relations. Such a project should be given wide publicity by means of exhibits and newspapers.
13. Financing the venture. Stock can be issued and sold. When the project has been completed, the shares can be bought up and the investment returned, perhaps with a dividend.
14. Selection of competent leadership in management positions. Discuss the requirements and qualifications.
15. Limited manpower. Some members of the class will have to double up on jobs.
16. Final evaluation of the project, including a summary of consumer reaction to the product.

Besides acquainting you with the basic fundamentals of American industry, a production project can give your industrial arts class the opportunity to be of service to the school and the community. For example, a quantity of toys might be manufactured for distribution to needy children at Christmas. Souvenir book ends, lamps, and such can be made for your school. Simple equipment can be made for other school classrooms—kindergarten building blocks, easels for art classes, and so forth.

CORPORATE ORGANIZATION

FOR A PRODUCTION MANUFACTURING PROJECT IN INDUSTRIAL ARTS

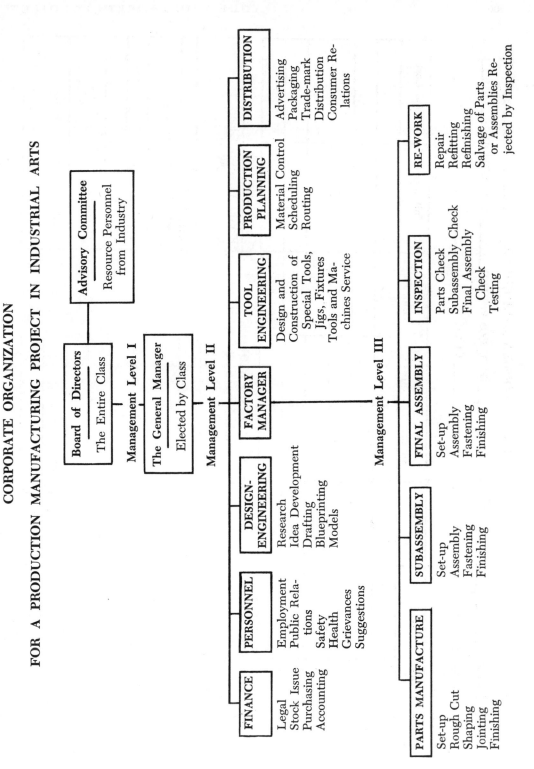

Board of Directors
The Entire Class

Advisory Committee
Resource Personnel from Industry

Management Level I

The General Manager
Elected by Class

Management Level II

FINANCE
Legal
Stock Issue
Purchasing
Accounting

PERSONNEL
Employment
Public Rela-
tions
Safety
Health
Grievances
Suggestions

**DESIGN-
ENGINEERING**
Research
Idea Development
Drafting
Blueprinting
Models

**FACTORY
MANAGER**

**TOOL
ENGINEERING**
Design and
Construction of
Special Tools,
Jigs, Fixtures
Tools and Ma-
chines Service

**PRODUCTION
PLANNING**
Material Control
Scheduling
Routing

DISTRIBUTION
Advertising
Packaging
Trade-mark
Distribution
Consumer Re-
lations

Management Level III

PARTS MANUFACTURE
Set-up
Rough Cut
Shaping
Jointing
Finishing

SUBASSEMBLY
Set-up
Assembly
Fastening
Finishing

FINAL ASSEMBLY
Set-up
Assembly
Fastening
Finishing

INSPECTION
Parts Check
Subassembly Check
Final Assembly
Check
Testing

RE-WORK
Repair
Refitting
Refinishing
Salvage of Parts
or Assemblies Re-
jected by Inspection

PROJECT DEVELOPMENT SCHEDULE

THE PROJECT _____ DATE BEGUN _____ DATE COMPLETED _____ DEVELOPER _____ SCHOOL _____

ESTIMATED TIME FOR COMPLETION _____ CLASS _____

PARTS LIST

Part No.	Name	Size	Bd. Ft.	Quantity Sq. Ft.	Lin. Ft.	Unit Cost	Total Cost

Cost of Materials _____

Finish, Abrasives, Glue, Screws, etc. 20% of Material Cost _____

Est. Project Cost _____

No. of Hrs. Consumed _____

Labor Cost/Hour _____

Total Labor Cost _____

Total Project Cost _____

APPROVED: _____

Final Grade: _____   Date: _____

MANUFACTURING SCHEDULE (STEPS)

1. _____
2. _____
3. _____
4. _____
5. _____
6. _____
7. _____
8. _____
9. _____
10. _____

TOOLS, MACHINES REQUIRED
(Check those on which you need instruction.)

1. _____
2. _____
3. _____
4. _____
5. _____
6. _____
7. _____
8. _____
9. _____
10. _____

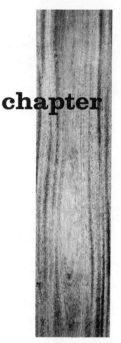

chapter **21**

IDEAS TO
DEVELOP

PROJECT IDEAS

The project ideas on the following pages are ideas only. None is perfect; all can be improved upon. Each is intended to suggest and to inspire, not merely to be copied.

Visit furniture stores, gift shops, toy stores, hobby shops, and museums to get ideas as to the number and variety of products made of wood. You will see some that are clever and unique, some well-designed, and perhaps some that should have been made of material other than wood. The project ideas which follow cannot include all of the kinds of things made of wood. They are representative of those that are particularly appropriate in wood.

Industrial arts is much more fun when everyone makes something different and each project shows a little of its maker's own ideas. You might develop a first-class project from a commonplace article—if you use fresh ideas with it. Or you might begin with an unusual idea like an invention.

Work out the details and make any change you think will help toward good design—toward a solution to a problem of function. Note the refinements (REF. I, etc.) given with some projects. Be sure to refine the idea before you start on the construction. Some information is not complete, to let you fill in the details you think are best.

Remember, it is your privilege and challenge to "cook-up" a better idea than any you may see in this book or elsewhere. Here is a starting point—where it may lead is up to you!

FLOOR VASES
for dried flowers, foliage, and seedlings

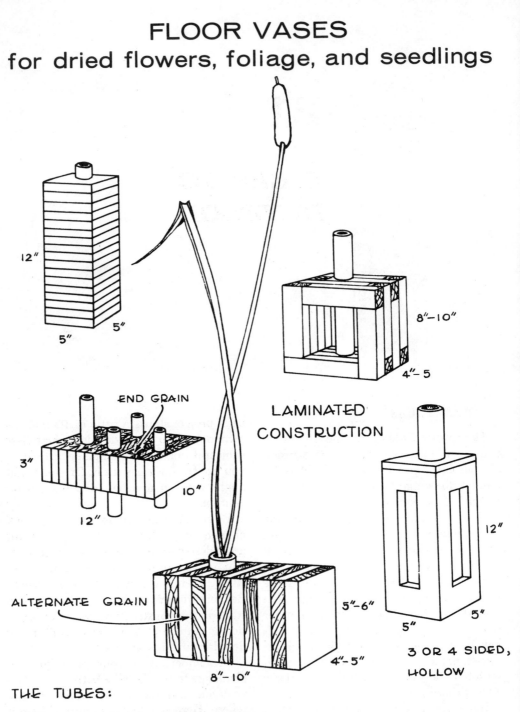

12"

5"

5"

8"–10"

4"–5"

LAMINATED
CONSTRUCTION

END GRAIN

3"

12"

10"

12"

ALTERNATE GRAIN

5"–6"

4"–5"

8"–10"

5"

5"

3 OR 4 SIDED,
HOLLOW

THE TUBES:

1"–1¼" DOWEL RODS, BORED OUT
AND PAINTED WITH FLAT BLACK.

FISH FORMS

MAKE A SCHOOL OF FISH
TO HANG ON A WALL.

PLAY WITH BRIGHT COPPER
WIRE FOR FINS.

EYES MAY BE CUT
THROUGH OR SHAPED IN
WOOD OF A CONTRASTING
COLOR.

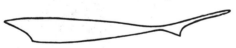

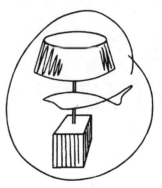

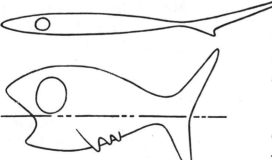

IMPALE A FISH ON A PIECE
OF $\frac{1}{8}''$ PIPE. SET THE PIPE IN
A RECTANGULAR BLOCK OF
WOOD FOR A LAMP BASE.

GIVE THE FISH A SCULPTURED
FORM.

CANDLE HOLDER

THE BASIC IDEA

YOU MAY PREFER A PLAIN BLOCK. WHEN SMOOTHED AND FINISHED, IT HAS A SIMPLE BEAUTY.

REF. I

BEVELING THE BLOCK EXPOSES MORE WOOD SURFACE.

REF. II

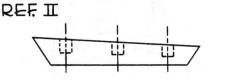

ADDING A TAPER NOT ONLY CHANGES THE SHAPE, BUT PRODUCES A DIFFERENT GRAIN PATTERN ON THE SURFACE AS WELL.

REF. III

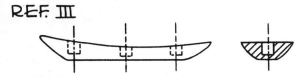

SCULPTURED TREATMENT REVEALS THE MOST BEAUTIFUL GRAIN.

REF. IV

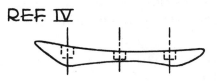

ADDING FEET GIVES A FEELING OF LIGHTNESS AND GRACE.

FREE FORMS CAN BE DRAWN
FROM GEOMETRIC SHAPES

LAYOUT THE GEOMETRIC SHAPE FULL SIZE.
SWING FAST, FLAT CURVES. ROUND THE CORNERS.

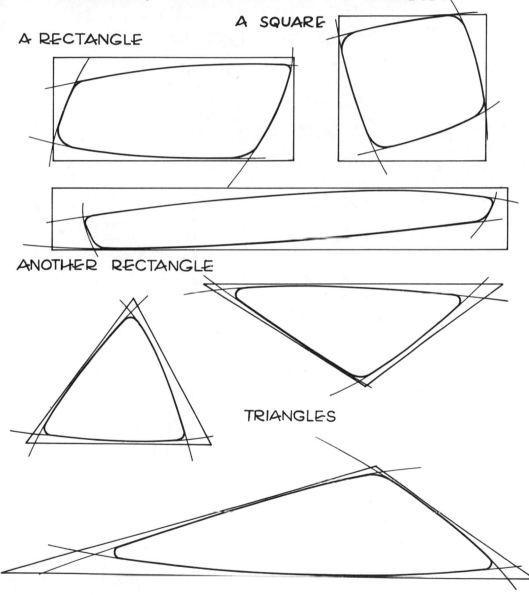

A SQUARE

A RECTANGLE

ANOTHER RECTANGLE

TRIANGLES

SUCH FREE FORMS ARE SUITABLE FOR COFFEE TABLE TOPS,
SCULPTURED TRAYS, LAMP BASES AND WHEREVER FREE FORMS
ARE APPROPRIATE.

A MOOD LIGHT

A BOX WITH PIERCED DESIGNS ON ITS SIDES WITH A FLUORESCENT STRIP LIGHT INSIDE

FIRST GET THE LIGHT, THEN PROPORTION THE BOX TO FIT.

MIX OR MATCH THE CUT OUTS.

MAKE THE ENDS REMOVABLE.

FASTEN. SIDES WITH LARGE-HEADED ESCUTCHEON PINS.

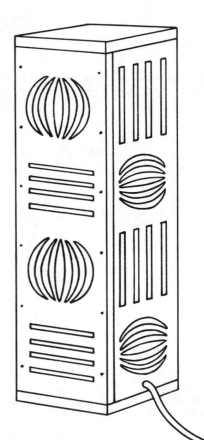

SERVING TRAYS

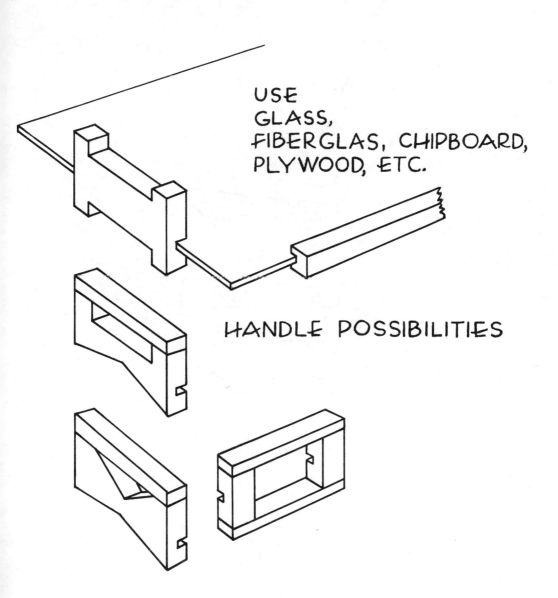

USE
GLASS,
FIBERGLAS, CHIPBOARD,
PLYWOOD, ETC.

HANDLE POSSIBILITIES

DESK SET

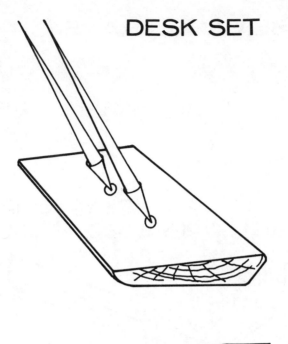

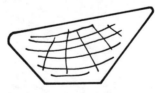

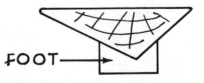

FOOT

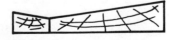

BOOK RACK

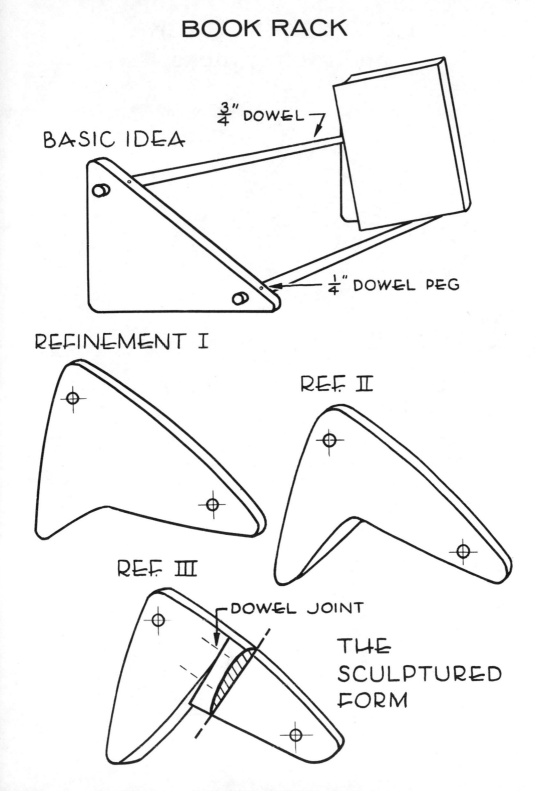

BASIC IDEA

$\frac{3}{4}$" DOWEL

$\frac{1}{4}$" DOWEL PEG

REFINEMENT I

REF. II

REF. III

DOWEL JOINT

THE SCULPTURED FORM

COMIC BOOK RACK
and 2 other racks

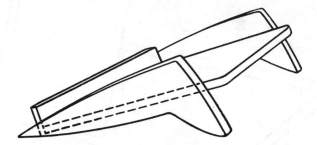

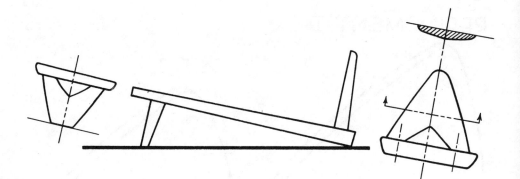

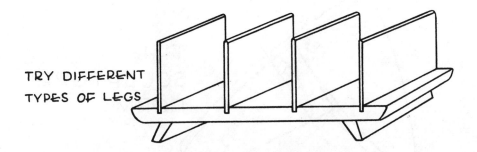

TRY DIFFERENT
TYPES OF LEGS

HOT DISH HOLDER CHEESE AND CUTTING BOARD

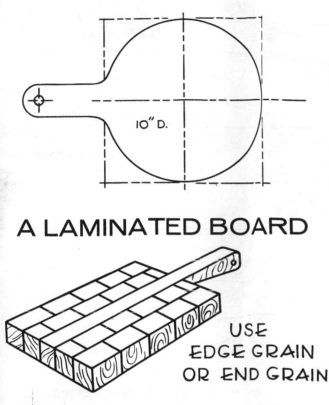

10" D.

SOME VARIATIONS

ROUND CORNERS

GOURD

WEDGE

SQUARE

A LAMINATED BOARD

USE
EDGE GRAIN
OR END GRAIN

TO USE END GRAIN: EDGE GLUE
LAMINATIONS INTO A BOARD OF
THE DESIRED WIDTH THEN
SURFACE BOTH FACES AND CUT
TO WIDTH. USE WATERPROOF GLUE.

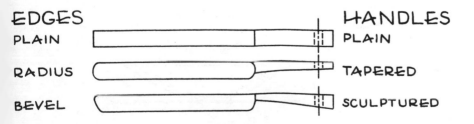

EDGES
PLAIN
RADIUS
BEVEL

HANDLES
PLAIN
TAPERED
SCULPTURED

SCULPTURED TRAYS

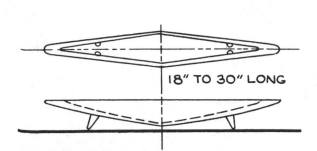

18" TO 30" LONG

MAKE THIS LONG
AND SLENDER
FROM A SOLID
PIECE OF WOOD.

HOLLOW CENTER
FIRST.

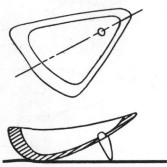

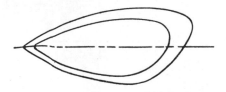

USE FREEFORM & GEOMETRIC
SHAPES FOR THE RICHEST
EFFECTS.

LEAF SHAPES TEND TO BE
TOO ORNATE, AND ARE TOO
ORDINARY.

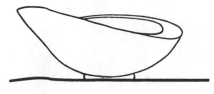

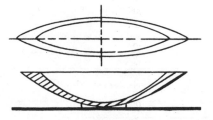

DOUBLE EASEL

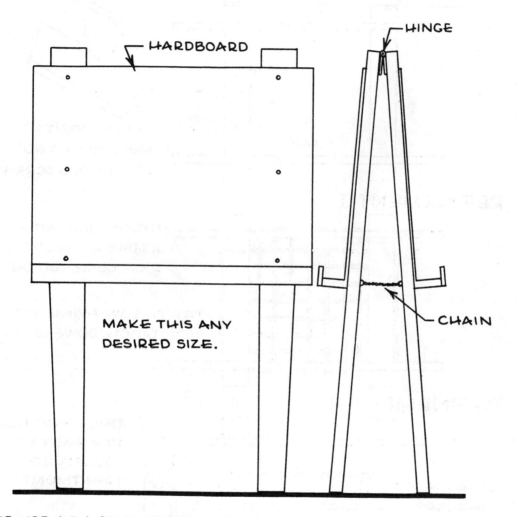

TO USE AS A CHALKBOARD APPLY 2 COATS OF CHALKBOARD PAINT TO ONE SIDE. LEAVE OTHER SIDE PLAIN TO USE WITH PAPER OR CANVAS AS A PAINTING EASEL.

WALL SHELF

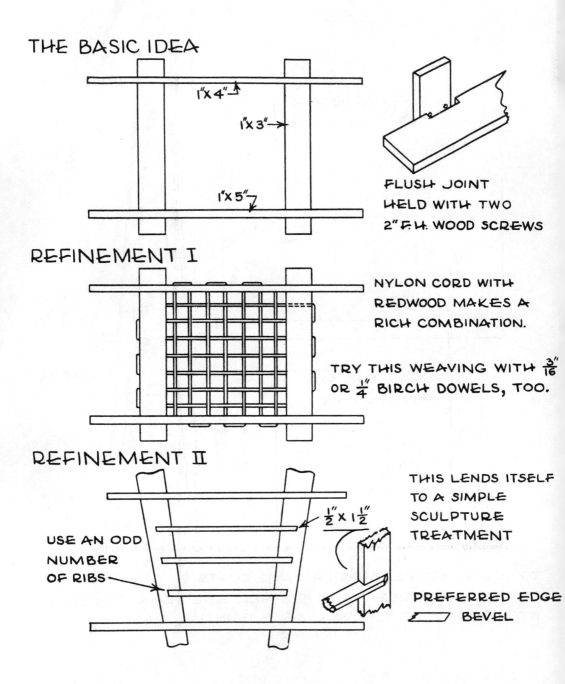

THE BASIC IDEA

$1'' \times 4''$
$1'' \times 3''$
$1'' \times 5''$

FLUSH JOINT
HELD WITH TWO
2" F. H. WOOD SCREWS

REFINEMENT I

NYLON CORD WITH
REDWOOD MAKES A
RICH COMBINATION.

TRY THIS WEAVING WITH $\frac{3}{16}''$
OR $\frac{1}{4}''$ BIRCH DOWELS, TOO.

REFINEMENT II

USE AN ODD
NUMBER
OF RIBS

$\frac{1}{2}'' \times 1\frac{1}{2}''$

THIS LENDS ITSELF
TO A SIMPLE
SCULPTURE
TREATMENT

PREFERRED EDGE
BEVEL

WALL SHELF
(refinements)

THE BASIC IDEA

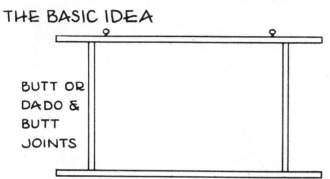

BUTT OR
DADO &
BUTT
JOINTS

REFINEMENT I

LAP
JOINTS

1X5 STOCK

1X4

1X6 STOCK

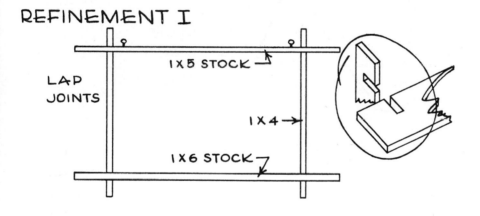

REFINEMENT II

WOVEN
BACK
RELIEVES
PLAINNESS
—ADDS
INTEREST

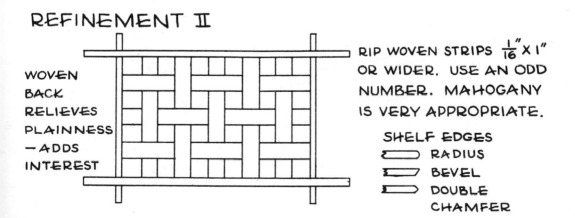

RIP WOVEN STRIPS $\frac{1}{16}"$X1"
OR WIDER. USE AN ODD
NUMBER. MAHOGANY
IS VERY APPROPRIATE.

SHELF EDGES

RADIUS

BEVEL

DOUBLE
CHAMFER

MAGAZINE RACK

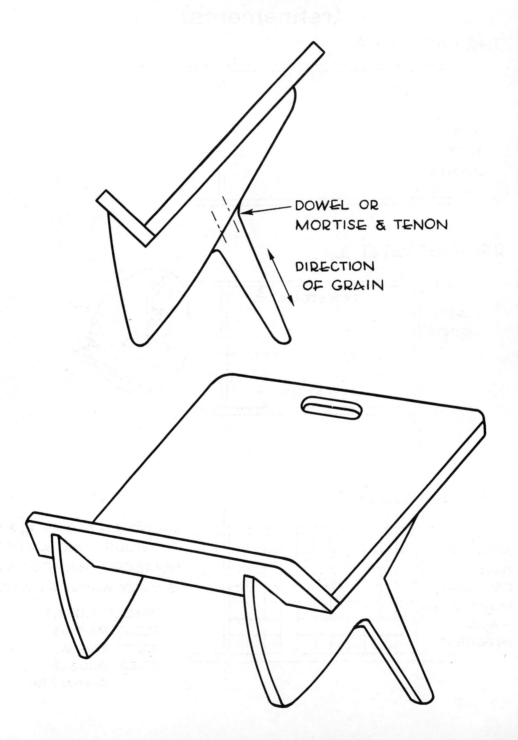

DOWEL OR
MORTISE & TENON

DIRECTION
OF GRAIN

MAGAZINE RACK

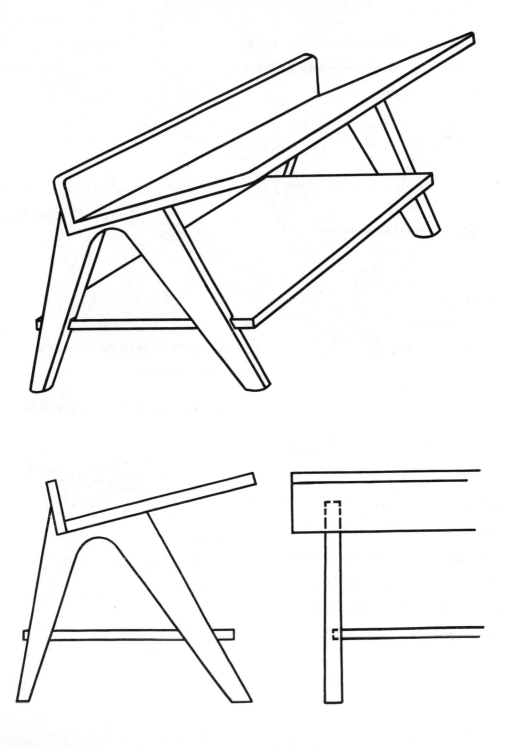

FOLDING MAGAZINE RACK

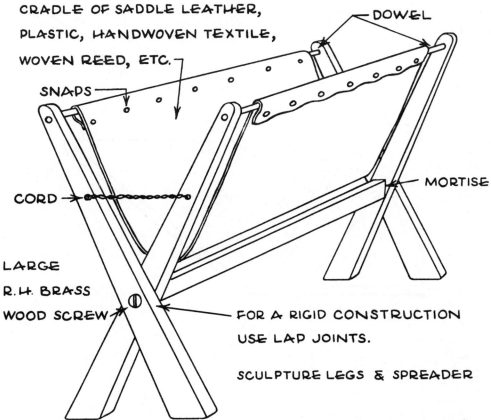

CRADLE OF SADDLE LEATHER,
PLASTIC, HANDWOVEN TEXTILE,
WOVEN REED, ETC.

DOWEL

SNAPS

CORD

MORTISE

LARGE
R.H. BRASS
WOOD SCREW

FOR A RIGID CONSTRUCTION
USE LAP JOINTS.

SCULPTURE LEGS & SPREADER

WITH A RIGID CONSTRUCTION
USE $\frac{1}{2}''$ X $1\frac{1}{2}''$ SPREADERS.
LACE NYLON CORD THROUGH
HOLES FOR THE CRADLE.
USE THROUGH MORTISE
AND TENON JOINTS.

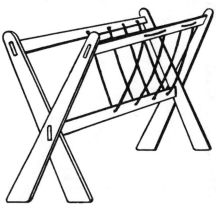

BIRD CAFETERIA

HOPPER TYPE

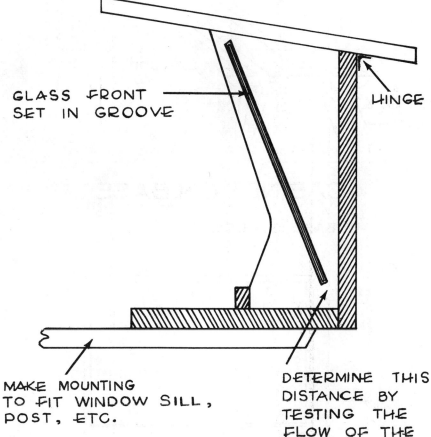

GLASS FRONT
SET IN GROOVE

HINGE

MAKE MOUNTING
TO FIT WINDOW SILL,
POST, ETC.

DETERMINE THIS
DISTANCE BY
TESTING THE
FLOW OF THE
GRAIN.

A BASE FOR A CABINET OR CHEST OF DRAWERS

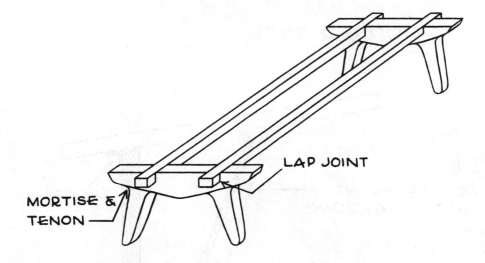

LAP JOINT

MORTISE &
TENON

CABINET ON BASE

THE BASE IS A LOW TABLE

CABINET BASE

THE CROSS PIECES ARE PUT CLOSER TOGETHER
TO MAKE THIS A COFFEE TABLE

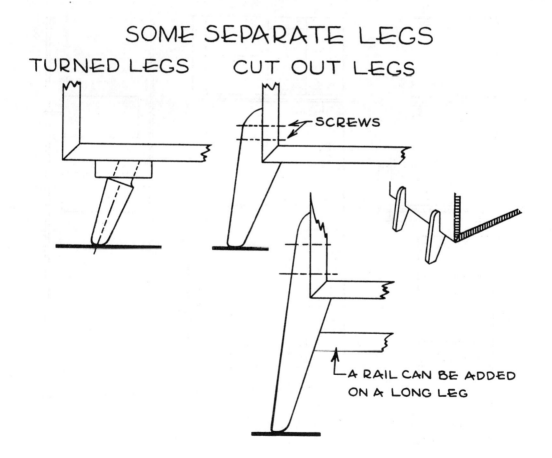

1 X 2 STOCK

CROSS PIECES: $\frac{3}{4}$" X 1"

SOME SEPARATE LEGS

TURNED LEGS   CUT OUT LEGS

SCREWS

A RAIL CAN BE ADDED
ON A LONG LEG

MODULAR UNIT FOR BOOKCASES

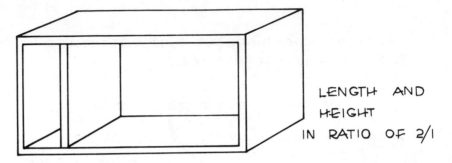

LENGTH AND
HEIGHT
IN RATIO OF 2/1

WHICH TYPE OF JOINT AT THE CORNERS?
WHICH FASTENER - GLUE, SCREWS, NAILS?

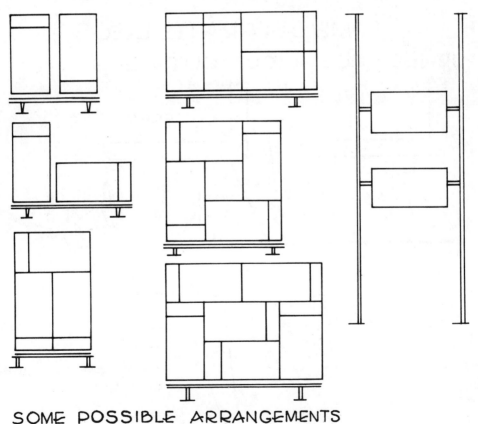

SOME POSSIBLE ARRANGEMENTS
HOW MANY OTHERS CAN YOU FIND?

LOW TABLES (coffee - end)

THE BASIC IDEA

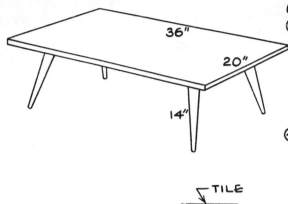

36"

20"

14"

TOP TYPES
① PLYWOOD
② GLUED UP STOCK
③ PLASTIC
  CEMENT PLASTIC TO
  PLYWOOD TOP WITH
  THE CONTACT CEMENT
  RECOMMENDED BY
  MFR.
④ TILE
  CORK FLOOR TILES
  MAKE A BEAUTIFUL
  TOP. USE RUBBER
  CEMENT.

TILE

MOLD →

A WOOD MOLDING SHOULD BE USED
AROUND THE EDGE WHEN PLASTIC
OR TILE TOPS ARE MADE.

REFINEMENT I

A BEVELED EDGE
MAKES THE TOP
APPEAR THICKER,
AND OVERCOMES THE
PLAINNESS OF THE
SQUARE EDGE.

DESIGN TIPS
① FIRST, DECIDE ON LENGTH, WIDTH, AND HEIGHT. THIS SIMPLE
   TABLE IDEA CAN BE EFFECTIVE AS A LOW, SQUATTY COFFEE
   TABLE, AND AN END TABLE, OR EVEN AS A DINING TABLE.
② THE LEGS SHOULD BE SPLAYED (SLANTED) IN TWO DIRECTIONS.
③ KEEP THE FOOT OF THE LEG EVEN WITH OR BACK FROM THE
   EDGE OF THE TOP; NEVER LET IT EXTEND BEYOND IT.

USE OF MOLDING (low tables cont.)

REFINEMENT II

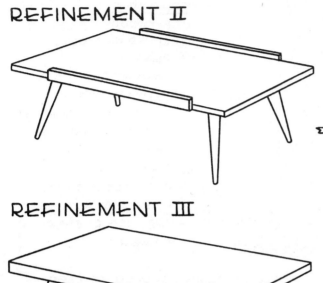

PARTIAL MOLD
THIS PARTIAL MOLD CAN BE SCULPTURED FOR ADDED EFFECT.

FULL MOLD
MOLDING ADDS REFINE-MENT TO A TABLE.

THE TOP APPEARS HEAVIER, BUT IT SHOULD NOT APPEAR OVERLY HEAVY.

USE MITER JOINTS AT CORNERS.

VENEER CAN BE GLUED TO THE EDGE OF A PLY-WOOD TOP FOR A VERY EFFECTIVE EDGE.

REFINEMENT III

REFINEMENT IV

A GLUED-UP TABLE TOP IS QUITE STRIKING.

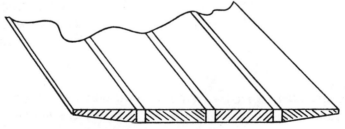

① USE EDGE GRAIN STRIPS FOR UNUSUAL QUALITY.
② USE NARROW, FLAT-GRAIN STOCK LAMINATED WITH STRIPS OF CONTRASTING COLOR.
③ BEVEL EDGES TO ADD LIGHTNESS AND INTEREST. TRY BEVEL-ING THE ENDS, TOO.

TABLE OR BASE FOR CABINET

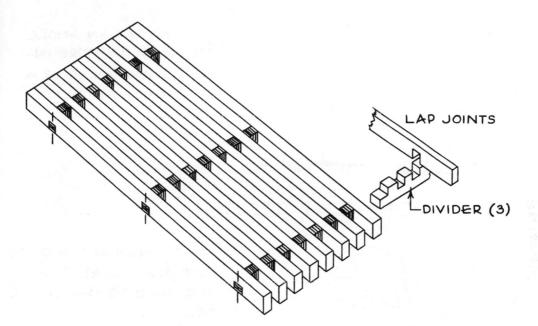

LAP JOINTS

DIVIDER (3)

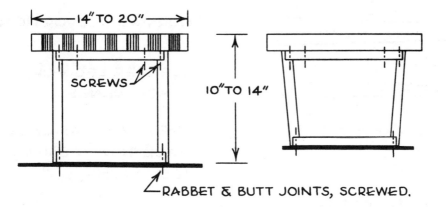

14" TO 20"

SCREWS

10" TO 14"

RABBET & BUTT JOINTS, SCREWED.

TO MAKE THE LAP JOINTS, CUT THE THREE DIVIDERS AT ONCE.

CLAMP THE SLATS TOGETHER AND CUT THEIR SLOTS AT ONCE.

SOME LEG DETAILS

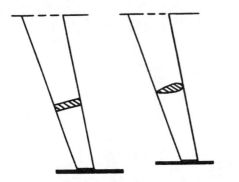

LEGS SET AT AN ANGLE ARE USUALLY MORE IN-TERESTING AND GIVE A FEELING OF STABILITY.

LEGS FROM FLAT STOCK

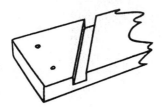

GLUE THEM INTO A DADO CUT IN A CLEAT TO BE SCREWED TO THE TABLE TOP.

TURNED LEGS

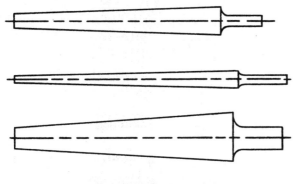

NORMAL PROPORTIONS.

SLENDER LEG FOR GRACEFULNESS.

THEY CAN EASILY BE MADE TOO MASSIVE, TOO STRONG.

SQUARE TAPERED LEGS

THIS SHAPE IS ALMOST ALWAYS APPROPRIATE.

TABLE AND BOOK SHELF

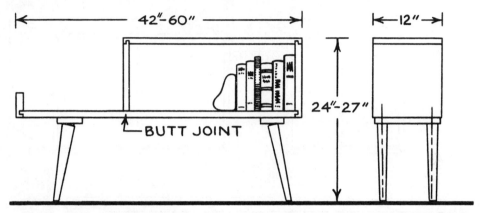

BUTT JOINT

LEGS SPLAYED ONE DIRECTION ONLY SO THAT TABLE
CAN FIT AGAINST WALL.

COFFEE TABLE

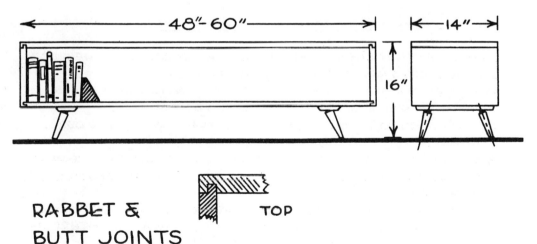

RABBET &
BUTT JOINTS

TOP

BOTTOM

DESIGN YOUR OWN CABINETS
AND CHEST OF DRAWERS

FEATURES UNITIZED CONSTRUCTION — BASE IS SEPARATE

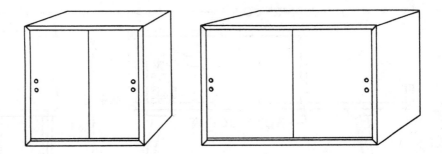

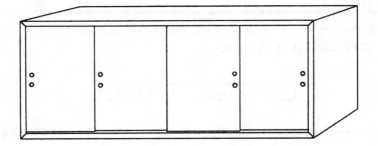

① CHOOSE PROPORTIONS ACCORDING TO THE FUNCTION OF THE PIECE.
② SLIDING DOORS SIMPLIFY THE CONSTRUCTION.
③ RABBET PLYWOOD OR HARDBOARD INTO BACK. FASTEN WITH BRADS.
④ CONSIDER THESE SUGGESTIONS FOR SLIDING DOORS:

   A. $\frac{1}{4}''$ PLYWOOD TO MATCH CABINET WOOD. THIS MAY TEND TO CURL,
      HOWEVER.

   B. WOOD VENEER CEMENTED TO HARDBOARD WITH CONTACT CEMENT,
      OR RUBBER CEMENT WORKS WELL. CLOTH-BACKED VENEER IS
      PREFERRED.

   C. MANY TEXTURES & PATTERNS OF HARDBOARDS ARE AVAILABLE.
      GET SAMPLES. THE ROUGH SURFACE OF PEGBOARD IS INTEREST-
      ING FOR DOOR FRONTS.

   D. PLASTIC VENEER AVAILABLE IN A VARIETY OF PATTERNS CAN
      BE CEMENTED TO HARDBOARD.

DETAILS OF SLIDING DOORS

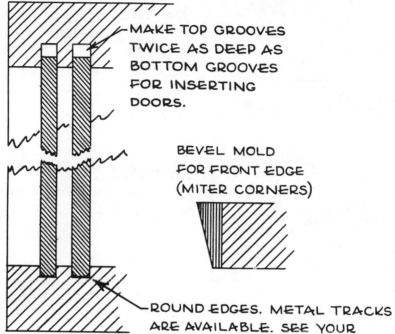

MAKE TOP GROOVES
TWICE AS DEEP AS
BOTTOM GROOVES
FOR INSERTING
DOORS.

BEVEL MOLD
FOR FRONT EDGE
(MITER CORNERS)

ROUND EDGES. METAL TRACKS
ARE AVAILABLE. SEE YOUR
HARDWARE CATALOG.

CORNER
CONSTRUCTION
RABBET & DADO

DRAWER GUIDES

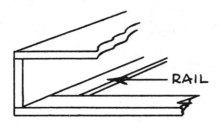

SIMPLEST
BOTTOM OF DRAWER SLIDES
ON RAIL.
MOST FRICTION — HARDEST
TO OPEN & CLOSE.
WAX PARTS WHICH RUB.

RAIL

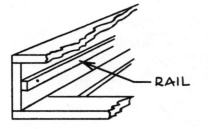

LESS FRICTION
GROOVE IN DRAWER SIDES
SLIDES ON RAIL.

RAIL

CENTER GUIDE

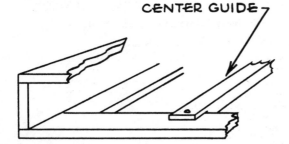

LEAST FRICTION
CARRIES LOAD OF
DRAWER & GUIDES IT.

SECTION THROUGH
DRAWER END

TRACK

MAKE A FREE FIT
WITH CENTER GUIDE
OF HARD WOOD.
GLUE TO BOTTOM OF
DRAWER AND MORTISE
IT INTO FRONT AND
BACK OF DRAWER.

DIVIDE THE INTERIOR TO SUIT YOUR NEEDS

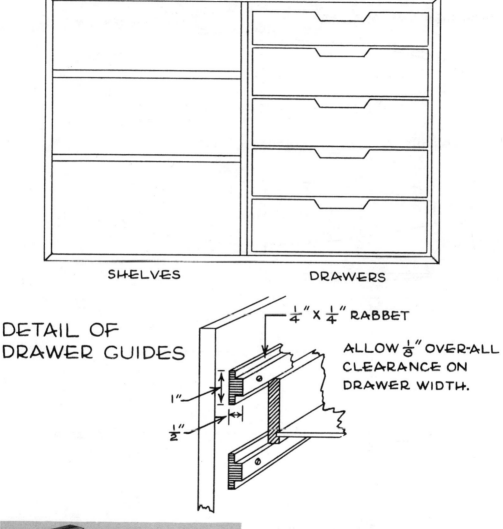

SHELVES   DRAWERS

DETAIL OF
DRAWER GUIDES

$\frac{1}{4}$" X $\frac{1}{4}$" RABBET

ALLOW $\frac{1}{8}$" OVER-ALL
CLEARANCE ON
DRAWER WIDTH.

1"

$\frac{1}{2}$"

MANUFACTURED DRAWER
SLIDES OF ALUMINUM,
WITH BALL BEARING ROLLERS
SIMPLIFY DRAWER CON-
STRUCTION AND IMPROVE
THE OPERATION.
Courtesy Trend Industries

COFFEE TABLES IN CONTEMPORARY STYLING

MAKE THEM LONG AND LEAN.

TRY DIFFERENT WIDTHS.

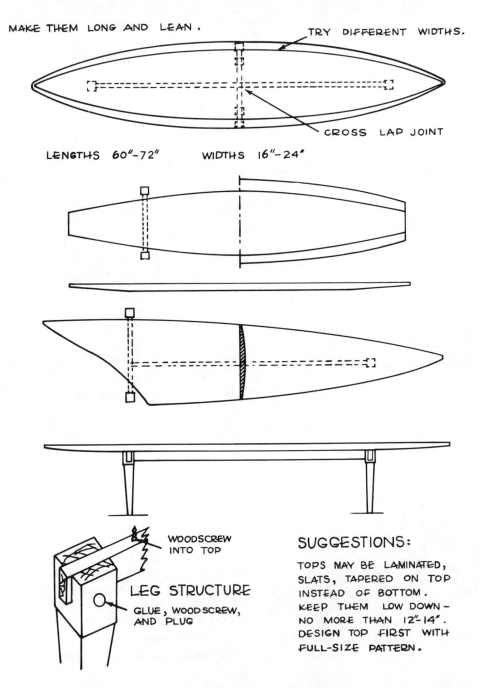

CROSS LAP JOINT

LENGTHS 60"–72"   WIDTHS 16"–24"

WOODSCREW INTO TOP

LEG STRUCTURE

GLUE, WOOD SCREW, AND PLUG

SUGGESTIONS:

TOPS MAY BE LAMINATED, SLATS, TAPERED ON TOP INSTEAD OF BOTTOM. KEEP THEM LOW DOWN – NO MORE THAN 12"–14". DESIGN TOP FIRST WITH FULL-SIZE PATTERN.

A SQUARE TABLE
WITH STRAIGHT — TURNED LEGS

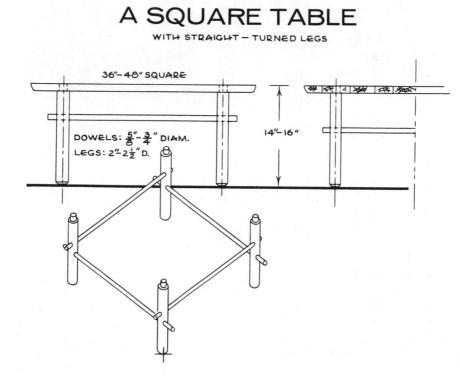

36"–48" SQUARE

DOWELS: $\frac{5}{8}$–$\frac{3}{4}$" DIAM.

LEGS: 2"–$2\frac{1}{2}$" D.

14"–16"

AN ARISTOCRAT OF TABLES
GRACEFUL, LIGHT, FORMAL — THE TOP SEEMS TO BE SUSPENDED

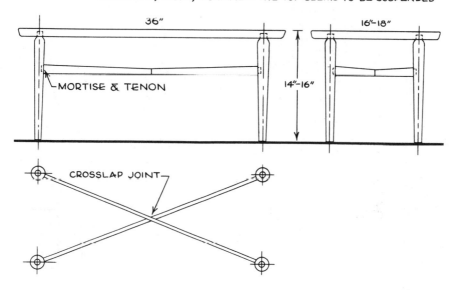

36"

16"–18"

MORTISE & TENON

14"–16"

CROSSLAP JOINT

A UTILITY TABLE

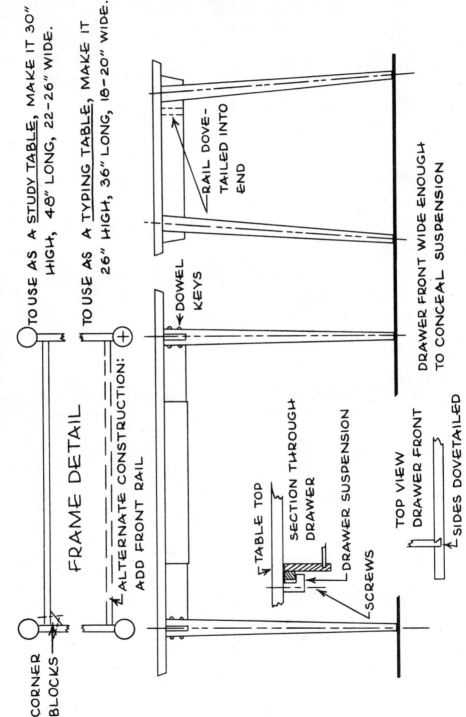

TO USE AS A STUDY TABLE, MAKE IT 30" HIGH, 48" LONG, 22-26" WIDE.

TO USE AS A TYPING TABLE, MAKE IT 26" HIGH, 36" LONG, 18-20" WIDE.

FRAME DETAIL

ALTERNATE CONSTRUCTION: ADD FRONT RAIL

CORNER BLOCKS

RAIL DOVE-TAILED INTO END

DOWEL KEYS

TABLE TOP

SECTION THROUGH DRAWER

DRAWER SUSPENSION

SCREWS

TOP VIEW DRAWER FRONT

SIDES DOVETAILED

DRAWER FRONT WIDE ENOUGH TO CONCEAL SUSPENSION

DESK

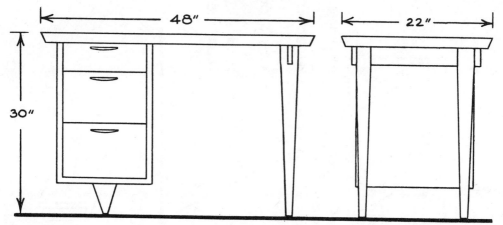

30"

48"   22"

MAKE DRAWER ASSEMBLY AS A UNIT.

SQUARE OR TURNED LEGS; MAKE CHAIR TO MATCH.

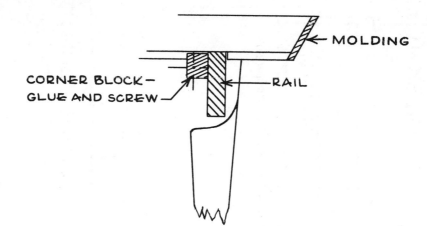

MOLDING

CORNER BLOCK —
GLUE AND SCREW

RAIL

LIBRARY OR DINING TABLE

2"X 3"RAILS

MORTISE
& TENON

30"

LEGS:
2X3 STOCK
SQUARE
TAPERED

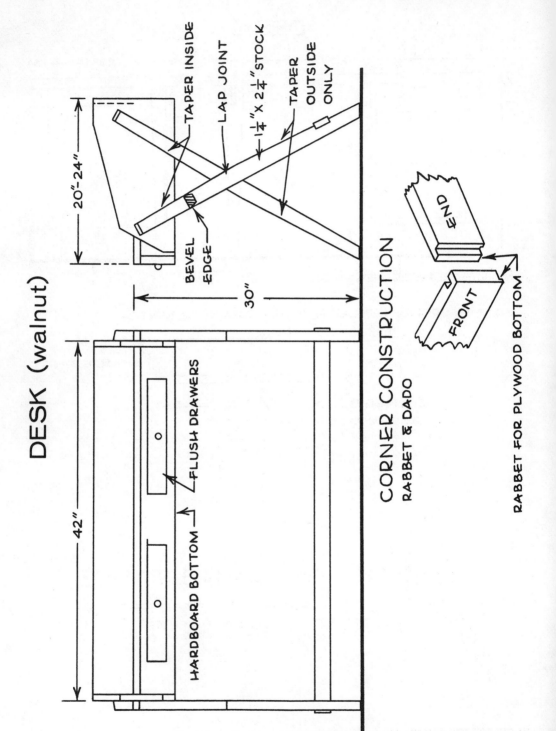

DESK (walnut)

TAPER INSIDE

LAP JOINT

1¼" X 2¼" STOCK

TAPER OUTSIDE ONLY

BEVEL EDGE

20"–24"

30"

42"

FLUSH DRAWERS

HARDBOARD BOTTOM

CORNER CONSTRUCTION

RABBET & DADO

END

FRONT

RABBET FOR PLYWOOD BOTTOM

A DESK CHASSIS

USING THIS BASIC IDEA FOR STRUCTURE, YOU CAN MAKE MANY DIFFERENT REFINEMENTS.

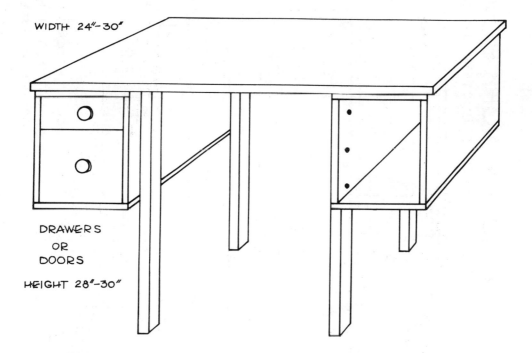

WIDTH 24"-30"

DRAWERS
OR
DOORS

HEIGHT 28"-30"

MAKE SIDE CABINETS ALIKE. EACH IS COMPLETELY ASSEMBLED, THEN SCREWED SECURELY TO THE UNDER SIDE OF THE TOP. THE LEGS ARE SCREWED TO THE CABINETS. THE LEGS CAN BE MADE OF WOOD OR SQUARE STEEL TUBING.

A HUSKY WORK BENCH
MADE FROM CONSTRUCTION LUMBER

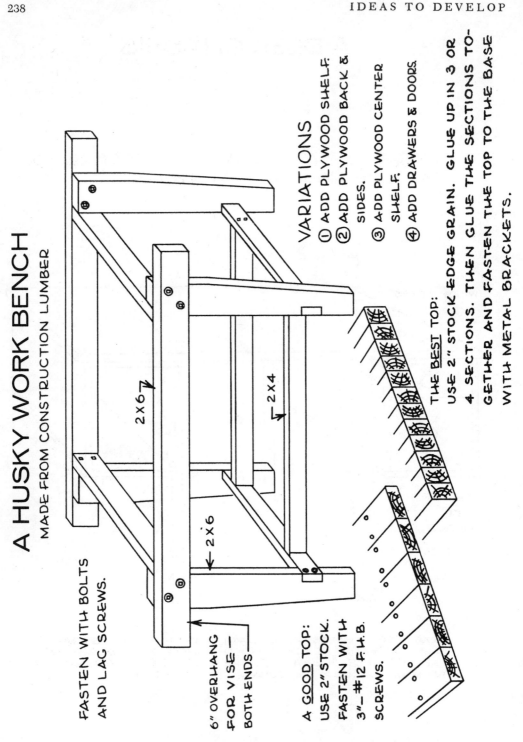

FASTEN WITH BOLTS
AND LAG SCREWS.

2 x 6

2 x 4

2 x 6

6" OVERHANG —
FOR VISE —
BOTH ENDS

A GOOD TOP:
USE 2" STOCK.
FASTEN WITH
3"– #12 F.H.B.
SCREWS.

VARIATIONS

1. ADD PLYWOOD SHELF.
2. ADD PLYWOOD BACK &
   SIDES.
3. ADD PLYWOOD CENTER
   SHELF.
4. ADD DRAWERS & DOORS.

THE BEST TOP:
USE 2" STOCK EDGE GRAIN. GLUE UP IN 3 OR
4 SECTIONS. THEN GLUE THE SECTIONS TO-
GETHER AND FASTEN THE TOP TO THE BASE
WITH METAL BRACKETS.

A HANDY WORK TABLE

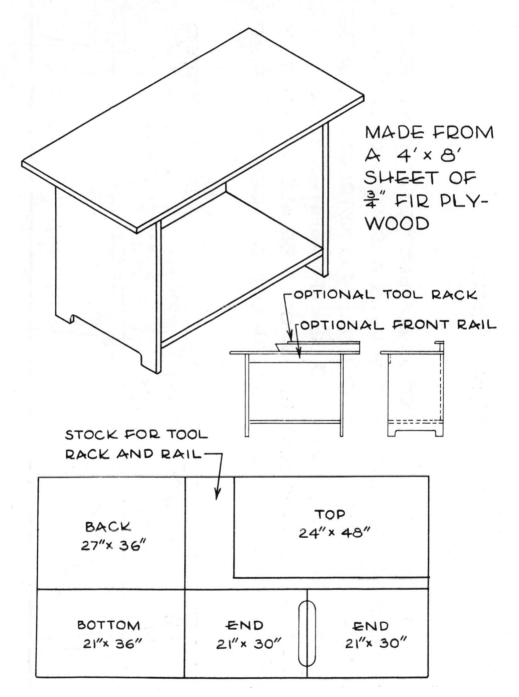

MADE FROM
A 4' x 8'
SHEET OF
¾" FIR PLY-
WOOD

OPTIONAL TOOL RACK

OPTIONAL FRONT RAIL

STOCK FOR TOOL
RACK AND RAIL

BACK
27"x 36"

TOP
24"x 48"

BOTTOM
21"x 36"

END
21"x 30"

END
21"x 30"

PICNIC BENCH

BUILD THIS FROM CONSTRUCTION LUMBER OR FROM REDWOOD PLANKS. USE $\frac{5}{16}''$ BOLTS, LAG SCREWS, AND WOOD SCREWS FOR A REALLY STURDY CONSTRUCTION. IF CONSTRUCTION LUMBER IS USED, THE TABLE SHOULD BE KEPT PAINTED. CREOSOTING WEATHERPROOFS TOO, BUT SHOULD BE ALLOWED TO DRY FOR SEVERAL MONTHS BEFORE USING. TREAT WITH PENTA.

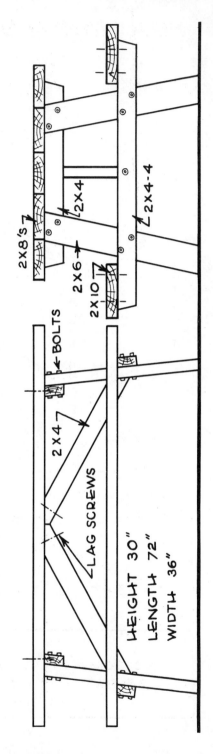

2X8'S

2X4

2X6

2X4-4

2X10

BOLTS

2X4

LAG SCREWS

HEIGHT 30"

LENGTH 72"

WIDTH 36"

A CHAIR FOR A RECREATION ROOM

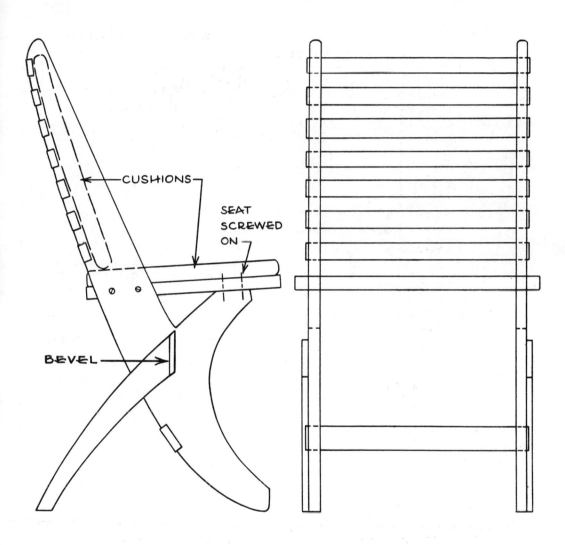

CUSHIONS

SEAT
SCREWED
ON

BEVEL

BASIC CHAIR

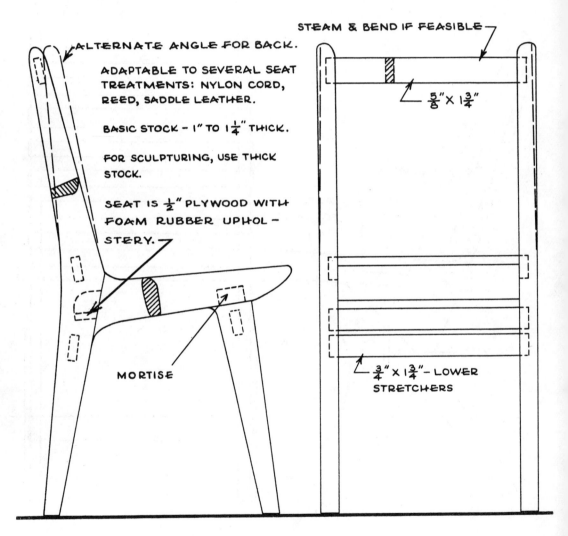

ALTERNATE ANGLE FOR BACK.

ADAPTABLE TO SEVERAL SEAT
TREATMENTS: NYLON CORD,
REED, SADDLE LEATHER.

BASIC STOCK – 1" TO 1$\frac{1}{4}$" THICK.

FOR SCULPTURING, USE THICK
STOCK.

SEAT IS $\frac{1}{2}$" PLYWOOD WITH
FOAM RUBBER UPHOL –
STERY.

MORTISE

STEAM & BEND IF FEASIBLE

$\frac{5}{8}$" X 1$\frac{3}{4}$"

$\frac{3}{4}$" X 1$\frac{3}{4}$" – LOWER
STRETCHERS

A BASIC CHAIR FOR
FOAM CUSHIONS

A GOOD IDEA FOR
MASS PRODUCTION.

OBTAIN THE DIMENSIONS SCIENTIFICALLY
MAKE A FULL-SIZE MOCK-UP.

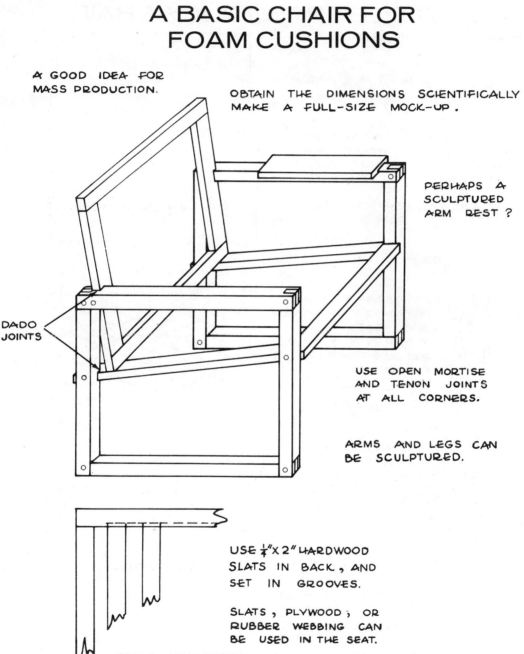

PERHAPS A
SCULPTURED
ARM REST ?

DADO
JOINTS

USE OPEN MORTISE
AND TENON JOINTS
AT ALL CORNERS.

ARMS AND LEGS CAN
BE SCULPTURED.

USE $\frac{1}{4}$"X 2" HARDWOOD
SLATS IN BACK, AND
SET IN GROOVES.

SLATS, PLYWOOD, OR
RUBBER WEBBING CAN
BE USED IN THE SEAT.

COULD YOU DESIGN A COUCH USING THIS CONSTRUCTION ?

A SIMPLE CROSS BUCK CHAIR

MAY BE USED WITH CROSS BUCK DESK

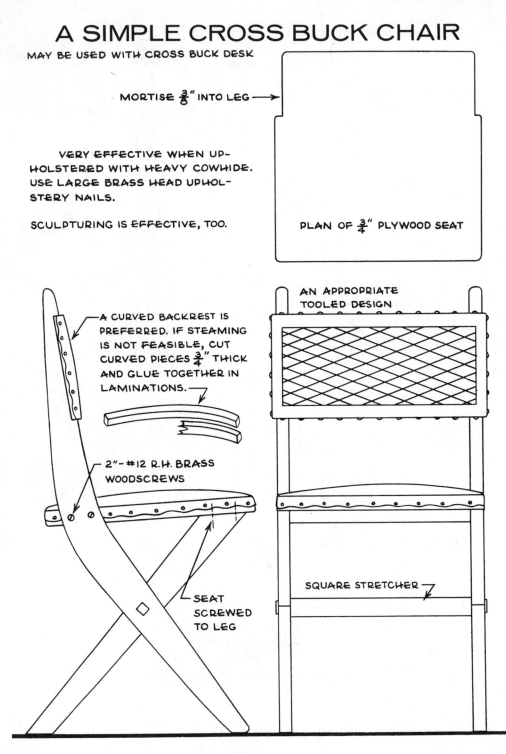

MORTISE 3/8" INTO LEG ——→

VERY EFFECTIVE WHEN UP-
HOLSTERED WITH HEAVY COWHIDE.
USE LARGE BRASS HEAD UPHOL-
STERY NAILS.

SCULPTURING IS EFFECTIVE, TOO.

PLAN OF 3/4" PLYWOOD SEAT

A CURVED BACKREST IS
PREFERRED. IF STEAMING
IS NOT FEASIBLE, CUT
CURVED PIECES 3/4" THICK
AND GLUE TOGETHER IN
LAMINATIONS.

2"-#12 R.H. BRASS
WOODSCREWS

SEAT
SCREWED
TO LEG

AN APPROPRIATE
TOOLED DESIGN

SQUARE STRETCHER

PORTABLE LAWN CHAIR

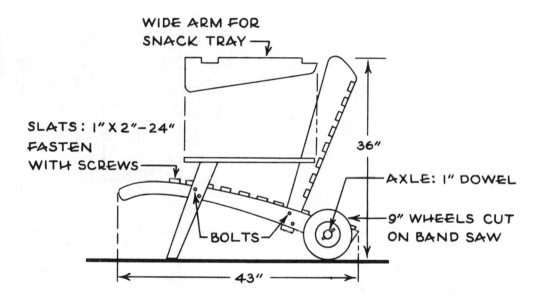

WIDE ARM FOR
SNACK TRAY

SLATS: 1" X 2"-24"
FASTEN
WITH SCREWS

36"

AXLE: 1" DOWEL

9" WHEELS CUT
ON BAND SAW

BOLTS

43"

NOTE

1" REDWOOD OR CYPRESS ARE FIRST CHOICE WOODS BECAUSE
THEY WEATHER BEST.

COMMON CONSTRUCTION LUMBER CAN BE USED BUT SHOULD
BE PAINTED.

COASTER WAGON WHEELS CAN BE USED.

FASTEN WITH WOOD SCREWS AND BOLTS; USE NO NAILS.

LOUNGE CHAIR
(with simple spring arrangement)

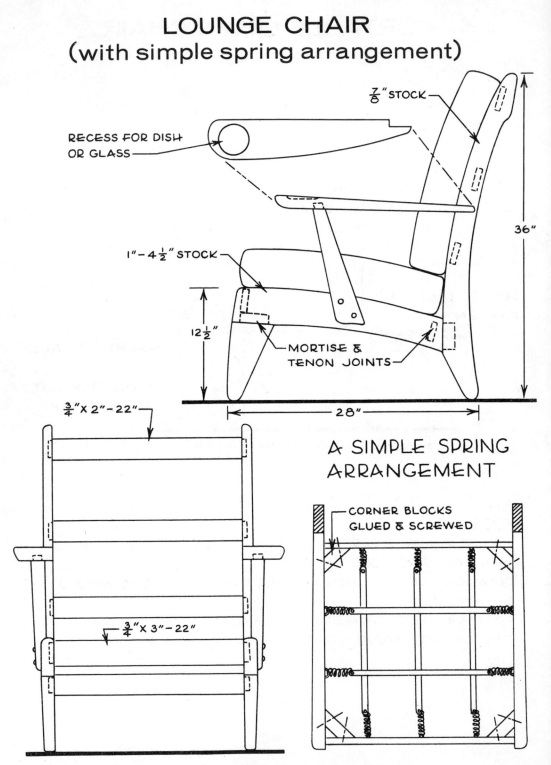

$\frac{7}{8}$" STOCK

RECESS FOR DISH
OR GLASS

36"

1"– 4$\frac{1}{2}$" STOCK

12$\frac{1}{2}$"

MORTISE &
TENON JOINTS

28"

$\frac{3}{4}$"X 2"–22"

$\frac{3}{4}$"X 3"–22"

A SIMPLE SPRING
ARRANGEMENT

CORNER BLOCKS
GLUED & SCREWED

TURNED BOWLS

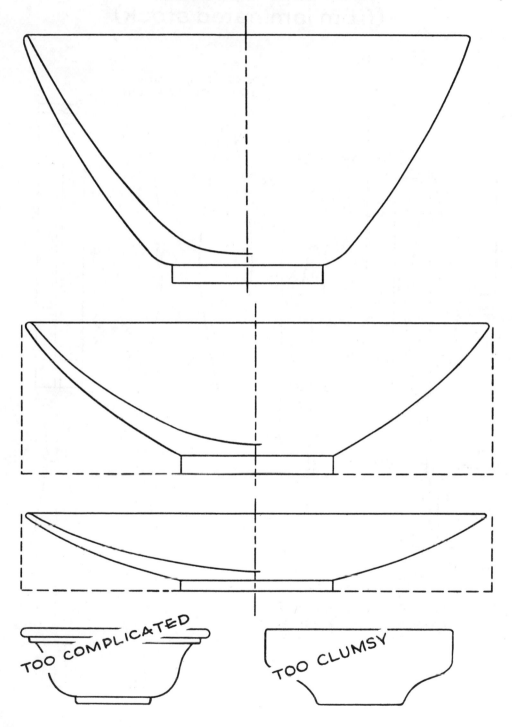

TOO COMPLICATED

TOO CLUMSY

TURNED LAMP BASES
(from laminated stock)

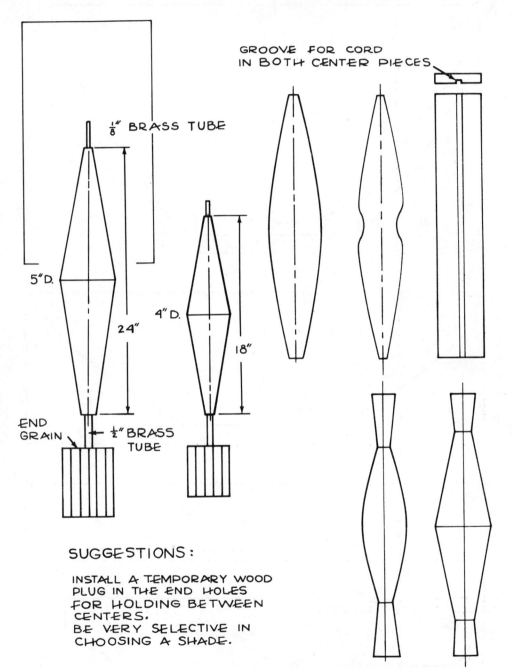

GROOVE FOR CORD
IN BOTH CENTER PIECES

$\frac{1}{8}$" BRASS TUBE

5" D.

24"

4" D.

18"

END
GRAIN

$\frac{1}{2}$" BRASS
TUBE

SUGGESTIONS:

INSTALL A TEMPORARY WOOD
PLUG IN THE END HOLES
FOR HOLDING BETWEEN
CENTERS.
BE VERY SELECTIVE IN
CHOOSING A SHADE.

TURNED STOOLS

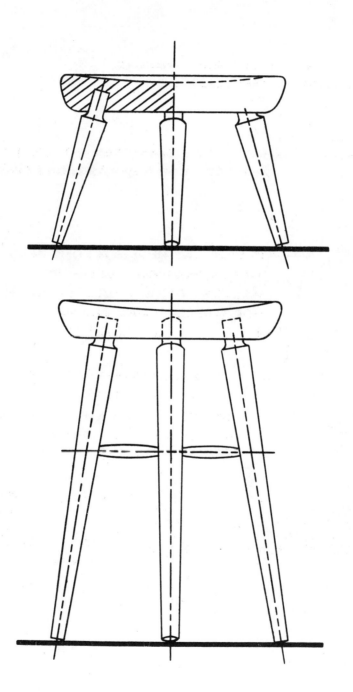

A FLOOR LAMP

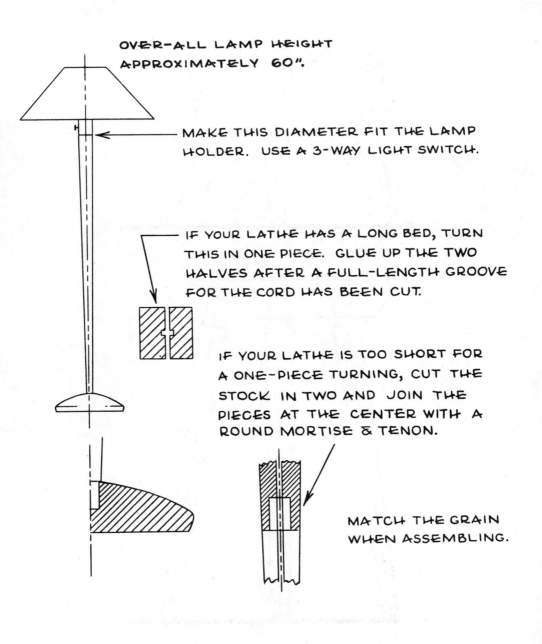

OVER-ALL LAMP HEIGHT APPROXIMATELY 60".

MAKE THIS DIAMETER FIT THE LAMP HOLDER. USE A 3-WAY LIGHT SWITCH.

IF YOUR LATHE HAS A LONG BED, TURN THIS IN ONE PIECE. GLUE UP THE TWO HALVES AFTER A FULL-LENGTH GROOVE FOR THE CORD HAS BEEN CUT.

IF YOUR LATHE IS TOO SHORT FOR A ONE-PIECE TURNING, CUT THE STOCK IN TWO AND JOIN THE PIECES AT THE CENTER WITH A ROUND MORTISE & TENON.

MATCH THE GRAIN WHEN ASSEMBLING.

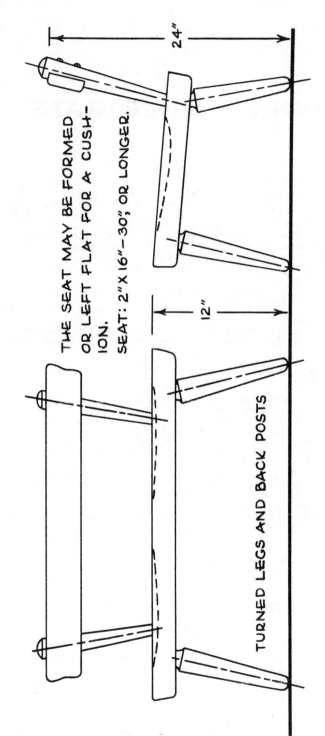

A FIREPLACE BENCH

THE SEAT MAY BE FORMED OR LEFT FLAT FOR A CUSHION.

SEAT: 2" X 16"—30", OR LONGER.

24"

12"

TURNED LEGS AND BACK POSTS

RESOURCE MATERIALS

BIBLIOGRAPHIES

Send for the following bibliographies listing sources of hundreds of books, booklets, charts, films, instructional kits, and project plans. Many of them are free to teachers.

1. *List of Publications on Chemistry of Wood and Derived Products.* Bulletin 238, October 1960. U. S. Department of Agriculture, Forest Products Laboratory, Madison, Wis.
2. *List of Publications on Glue, Glued Products, and Veneer.* Bulletin 513, July 1962. U. S. Department of Agriculture, Forest Products Laboratory, Madison, Wis.
3. *List of Publications on Wood Finishing Subjects.* Bulletin 454, May 1960. U. S. Department of Agriculture, Forest Products Laboratory, Madison, Wis.
4. *Lumber Literature.* National Lumber Manufacturers Association, 1319 Eighteenth St., N.W., Washington 6, D.C.
5. *An Outline for Teaching Conservation.* U. S. Department of Agriculture. Soil Conservation Service, Washington 6, D.C.
6. *School Bibliography.* American Forest Products Industries, Inc., 1319 Eighteenth St., N.W., Washington 6, D.C.
7. *Uses, Properties, and Identification of American Woods and American Lumber Industry.* Inquiry Reference Service, U. S. Department of Commerce, Washington 25, D.C.

REFERENCES

The industrial arts library should include these authentic references:

1. *Chemical Conversion Products from Wood.* Bulletin 2179, August 1960. U. S. Department of Agriculture, Forest Products Laboratory, Madison, Wis.
2. *Changing Utilization of Hardwoods.* Bulletin 2244, April 1962. U. S. Department of Agriculture, Forest Products Laboratory, Madison, Wis.
3. *Forest Resources Handbook.* American Forest Products Industries, Inc., 1319 Eighteenth St., N.W., Washington 6, D.C.
4. *Partial List of Publications for Furniture Manufacturers, Woodworkers, and Teachers of Wood Shop Practice.* Bulletin No. 1775. Forest Products Laboratory, Madison, Wis.
5. *Products of American Forests.* A Forest Products Laboratory publication available from: Superintendent of Documents, U.S. Government Printing Office, Washington 25, D.C.
6. *Symposium on Adhesives for the Wood Industry.* Bulletin 2183, January 1960. U.S. Department of Agriculture, Forest Products Laboratory, Madison, Wis.
7. *Symposium on Fastenings for Wood in House Construction.* Bulletin 2241, February 1962. U. S. Department of Agriculture, Forest Products Laboratory, Madison, Wis.
8. *Wood Handbook, No. 72.* A Forest Products Laboratory publication available from: Superintendent of Documents, U.S. Govt. Printing Office, Washington 25, D.C. 1955.

SELECTED BOOKS AND BOOKLETS

1. Barocci, Louis et al. *Instructional Units in Hand Woodwork.* Milwaukee: Bruce Publishing Co.
2. *Buyers' Specification—Latex Foam.* Technical details and characteristics of latex foam, available from the Rubber Manufacturers Association, Inc., 444 Madison Ave., New York 22, New York.
3. *Civilization Through Tools.* Des Plaines, Ill.: The Wilkie Foundation.
4. De Cristoforo, R. J. *Power Tool Woodworking for Everyone.* Cincinnati, Ohio: Magna-American Corporation.
5. Douglass, J. H. *Woodworking with Machines.* Bloomington, Ill.: McKnight and McKnight Publishing Co.
6. Feier, J. L. *Industrial Arts Woodworking.* Peoria, Ill.: Charles A. Bennett Co., Inc.

7. Fryklund, Verne C. and La Berge, Armand J. *General Shop Bench Woodworking*. Bloomington, Ill.: McKnight and McKnight Publishing Co.
8. Groneman, Chris H. *General Woodworking*. New York: McGraw-Hill Book Co., Inc.
9. Gross, Fred, ed. *How to Work with Tools and Wood*. New York: Pocket Books, Inc.
10. Hammond, James J. and others. *Woodworking Technology*. Bloomington, Ill.: McKnight and McKnight Publishing Co.
11. Hjorth, Herman. *Modern Machine Woodworking*. Milwaukee: Bruce Publishing Co.
12. *How to Glue It*. The Franklin Glue Co., Columbus, Ohio.
13. *How to Work with Airfoam*. Goodyear Tire and Rubber Co., Airfoam Division, Akron, Ohio.
14. *Related Information for the Wood Area*. Albany, N. Y.: Delmar Publishers, Inc.
15. *Resilient Urethane Foam Made with Du Pont Hylene*. A booklet describing properties and uses of urethane foam, available from the E. I. Du Pont De Nemours Co., Inc., Wilmington, Del.
16. *Sandpaper—How and Why*. New York: Behr-Manning.
17. Soderberg, George A. *Finishing Materials and Methods*. Bloomington, Ill.: McKnight and McKnight Publishing Co.
18. *The Use of Hand Tools and Portable Machinery*. Albany, N. Y.: Delmar Publishers, Inc.
19. Van Doren, Harold. *Industrial Design*. New York: McGraw-Hill Book Co., Inc.
20. Wagner, Willis H. *Woodworking*. Chicago: Goodheart-Willcox Co., Inc.
21. Walton, Harry. *How to Choose and Use Power Tools*. A Black and Decker handbook. New York: Popular Library.

PERIODICALS

1. *Craft Horizons,* monthly by American Craftsman's Council, 44 W. 53rd St., New York 19. Includes "Forum", a Swedish magazine dealing with furniture, interior decoration, textiles, pottery, glass, metal work.
2. *Furniture Design and Manufacturing,* monthly by Graphic Arts Publishing Co., 608 So. Dearborn St., Chicago 5. A trade journal.
3. *Industrial Design,* monthly by Whitney Publications, Inc., 18 East 50th St., New York 22. A magazine for the professional designer.
4. *Interiors,* monthly by Whitney Publications, Inc., 18 East 50th St., New York 22. A magazine for interior decorators and architects.
5. *Wood and Wood Products,* monthly by Vance Publishing Co., 593 Monroe St., Chicago 3, Ill. A trade journal.
6. *Wood Working Digest,* monthly by Hitchcock Publishing Co., Wheaton, Ill. A trade journal.

Index